# The Student Edition of
# MICRO-CAP IV™

# The Student Edition of
# MICRO-CAP IV™

An electronic circuit analysis program . . .
*adapted for education*

## Martin S. Roden

California State University, Los Angeles

## The Benjamin/Cummings Publishing Company, Inc.

Redwood City, California • Menlo Park, California
Reading, Massachusetts • New York • Don Mills, Ontario
Wokingham, U.K. • Amsterdam • Bonn • Sydney
Singapore • Tokyo • Madrid • San Juan

Benjamin/Cummings makes every effort to publish high-quality educational materials. If you have any comments regarding the contents of this manual, we would like to hear them. Please send them to: The Benjamin/Cummings Publishing Company, Electrical Engineering Editor, 390 Bridge Parkway, Redwood City, CA 94065.

The Student Edition of MICRO-CAP IV is published by The Benjamin/Cummings Publishing Company, Inc.

The Student Edition of MICRO-CAP IV was developed and programmed by Spectrum Software, Inc.

Roden, Martin S.
        The student edition of MICRO-CAP IV / Martin S. Roden.
            p.        cm.
        Includes index.
        ISBN 0-8053-1718-X (pbk.)
            1.  Micro-Cap IV  2.  Electronic circuit design -- Data processing.
        3.  Electronic circuit analysis -- Data processing.  I. Title.
        TK7867.R65  1993
        621.3815'0285'5369 -- dc20                            92-41039
                                                                  CIP


ISBN   0-8053-1718-X
       0-201-94286-6


3  4  5  6  7  8  9  10  DO  9594


The Benjamin/Cummings Publishing Company, Inc.
390 Bridge Parkway
Redwood City, California  94065

# Preface

## To the Student

Welcome to the world of computer-based circuit analysis with MICRO-CAP IV. The Student Version of MICRO-CAP IV is an analog circuit simulator based on the SPICE 2G.6 numerical algorithms. MICRO-CAP IV makes it exceptionally easy to enter your circuits into a personal computer because the entry process is menu-driven—the circuit schematic unfolds before your eyes as you interact directly with the software. The program uses screens with pull-down menus and mouse support. It is easy to interface with SPICE circuit text files. Waveforms are displayed in real time, so you can terminate runs without waiting for completion. You can probe the schematic for various waveforms or use a scope feature to examine details of a simulation result.

Circuit simulation programs are extremely useful in design. A real-life circuit does not behave exactly as the ideal theory predicts. Simplified models of elements and devices exclude many of the more complex dependencies that occur when the circuit is constructed. Computer simulation programs allow you to check the performance of a circuit before building it. You can easily make changes in the circuit at this stage since you need only change the input to the computer program. You avoid a lot of time and expense, and you can fine-tune your design for optimum performance. You can perform multiple simulations to examine the worst possible case, or find the probability that a component or system will fail.

You have purchased the Student Version of a software package used by engineering professionals. The graduating engineer cannot survive in the technological world without an understanding of, and familiarity with, the use of the computer as a design tool. Computer-aided engineering (CAE) is an integral part of electrical engineering. Designers use state-of-the-art computer systems to optimize component selection. Even small personal computers can aid in checking designs and indicating which parameters require modification.

MICRO-CAP IV is becoming the industry standard for use in electronic circuit design. Very minor differences exist between the Student Version and the Professional Version of this software: The Student Version limits the number of circuit nodes to 50, while the Professional Version easily handles circuits as large as 10,000 nodes. The Professional Version includes a MODEL program, which is an interactive program that takes numbers from data sheet graphs or tables and produces an optimized set of device model parameters. This MODEL program is not included in the Student Version. The Student Version libraries of pre-entered devices (such as bipolar transistors) are limited to the most common devices, although you can add any device to the library. MICRO-CAP IV's SPICE-based circuit analysis program contains models of many popular electronic devices. This program forms an ideal base for a student-oriented electronic circuit-design program—not only because students will use the Professional Version after they graduate, but also because the program's general features are representative of a broad class of analysis software.

A word of caution is appropriate if this is your first experience with simulation. Just as the proliferation of calculators did not eliminate the need to understand the theory of mathematics, electronic circuit simulation programs do not eliminate the need to understand electronic theory. As in the case of calculators, MICRO-CAP IV can free the engineer from tedious calculations, freeing more time for doing the kind of creative work a computer cannot do.

Before performing a computer analysis of a network, you should have some idea of what to expect. We suggest you use this software to check your designs. In the process you may uncover some unexpected results, because a paper design rarely incorporates models as sophisticated as those used by this program.

To keep down the price and make this software available to more students, we have intentionally eliminated some material from this manual. For example, although the Student Version and Professional Version operate in essentially the same ways, the manual you are holding is less than 250 pages long while the documentation accompanying the Professional Version spans about 500 pages. Not every fine point of the simulation is covered in this student manual. Experimentation and the help screens should fill in many of the blanks. We hope your instructor can provide any missing details.

## To the Instructor

As indicated in "To the Student," this manual is intended to cover the most important features of the MICRO-CAP IV software. It is intentionally not as comprehensive as the documentation accompanying the Professional Version. Spectrum Software is making the Professional Version documentation available for purchase by instructors adopting the Student Version for their classes.

Also available to instructors, without cost, is an instructor's manual illustrating detailed solutions to the problems following each tutorial. In addition to these solutions, the manual discusses the solutions and any deviations from results predicted by theory.

## Objectives

The primary objectives of *The Student Edition of MICRO-CAP IV* are as follows:

- To provide a tool for handling the tedious calculations of circuit design, thus affording you more time for creative design work.

- To help you design circuit boards for your course work and prepare you for using MICRO-CAP IV in your profession.

- To provide a package that has been carefully designed to save you money while not compromising features significant at this phase in your education.

## Features

*The Student Edition of MICRO-CAP IV* includes the following features:

- A library of standard passive and active devices, including popular models of BJTs, MOSFETs, JFETs, op-amps, and diodes.

- The capacity to custom-define devices and add them to the library for later use.

- Three types of analysis: transient analysis, ac analysis, and dc analysis. Within each of these types of analysis, you can perform iterative analysis (temperature stepping and parameter stepping), PROBE analysis where you can display multiple waveforms by clicking the mouse at the appropriate points in the circuit, and Monte Carlo probabilistic analysis to provide for random variation of device parameters.

## Organization of this Manual

The Student Version manual is organized into three parts: Part I, "Getting Started", contains introductory information and instructions for entering the programs. It also contains a simple example so you can experience the features of the program within minutes of setting it up on your computer.

Part II, "Tutorials," is the heart of the manual. It contains examples and models, giving you a feel for the software's versatility and motivating a more in-depth approach as you progress. Each tutorial reinforces instruction with examples and problems. Part III, "Reference," contains three sections. The first section contains a listing of error messages. The second part illustrates the various keyboard commands for those not wishing to use a mouse. The final section discusses use of the conversion program to import files from earlier versions of MICRO-CAP.

## Acknowledgments

Over 25,000 copies of the Student Edition of MICRO-CAP III have been used by students in universities throughout the country. We appreciate the high degree of response we received from users whose input has contributed to the development and refinement of the software and manual.

We owe a sincere thanks to Lt. Colonel Al Batten and his students at the U.S. Air Force Academy, Colorado. Lt. Colonel Batten provided a great deal of guidance and insight in his reviews of both MICRO-CAP III and the current version, MICRO-CAP IV.

We would also like to thank Dr. Roy Barnett of California State University, Los Angeles, an avid user of MICRO-CAP III who provided a series of detailed and critical reviews of MICRO-CAP IV.

Walter Schwab and Gerry Tapper of Northeastern deserve a note of thanks for their debugging efforts with the beta version of the software.

The software was developed by Spectrum Software of Sunnyvale, California. Andy Thompson, Tim O'Brien, and John Szymanski spent long hours responding to student needs and carefully reviewing all aspects of the project and the manual.

At Benjamin/Cummings, the following people worked diligently to make this manual as student-friendly and clean as possible: Jennifer Young, Acquisitions Editor; Laura Cheu, Editorial Assistant; and Megan Rundel, Production Coordinator. A special thanks also goes out to Tim Spaid, Technical Support Supervisor at Addison-Wesley.

This manual was written by one of the authors of the text *Electronic Design, Circuits and Systems, Second Edition,* by C. J. Savant Jr., Martin S. Roden, and Gordon L. Carpenter (Benjamin/Cummings, 1991). While *The Student Edition of MICRO-CAP IV* stands by itself, the wide variety of design approaches and examples in the textbook will serve as a valuable adjunct.

I am confident that you will find this package to be educational, exciting, and very useful. We welcome your comments.

Martin S. Roden
California State University, Los Angeles

# Contents

---

## Part II    Tutorials

# The Student Edition of
# MICRO-CAP IV™

# GETTING STARTED

# 1

# Before You Begin

In this chapter we describe the contents of the Student Edition of the MICRO-CAP IV package and the typographical conventions of this book. You should read this carefully before you attempt to use or install the program.

## Checking Your Computer Setup

Minimum hardware requirements are as follows:

- An 80286 IBM compatible computer
- DOS version 3.3 or later
- 640K of RAM
- A Hercules, EGA, VGA, or MCGA display adapter and monitor
- A 1.2M disk drive or a 720K disk drive
- A Microsoft or compatible mouse
- A hard drive with at least 2MB available (Note: After installation, the program uses less than 1.5MB of hard disk space, but you must have 2MB for installation.)

# Checking Your MICRO-CAP IV Package

The Student Edition of MICRO-CAP IV includes

- Student user manual
- Warranty registration card
- Two 720K program disks or one 1.2M program disk containing the following files:

INSTALL.BAT

STUDENT.ZIP

PKUNZIP.EXE

These files are compressed. After you run the installation, you will have eight files in a main MC4S directory:

MC4S.EXE

MC4.DAT

CS.MC4

TOSPICE.EXE

CONVERT.EXE

STUDENT.DOC

MC4C.EXE

MC4E.EXE

In addition, a subdirectory labeled DATA contains close to 100 files consisting of sample circuits and libraries.

# Product Support

Telephone assistance is available from Addison-Wesley to registered instructors who have adopted the Student Edition of MICRO-CAP IV. Technical support is not provided directly to the student. If you have a software problem that is not answered in this student manual or by the help screens, then ask your instructor for assistance.

# Typographical Conventions and Definitions

Keystrokes that you must type are designated in this manual by boldface type (for example, **PULSE**). Note that while this manual often uses upper- and lowercase letters, the program does not recognize the difference.

The following terms are used in this manual:

**Type** The keystrokes to be typed are in a bold typeface. For example:

Type **PULSE**

If you are asked to enter several keystrokes in sequence, such as

Type **A** and then type **PULSE.**

then, to conserve space, the commands often are shown on one line separated by semicolons. Do not type the semicolons when entering the commands; the semicolons are there just to symbolize a slight pause between entering each pair of commands. For example:

Type **A; PULSE**

A + sign between key names indicates that keys are to be pressed simultaneously. Thus Shift+F2 means that you hold down the Shift key while pressing the F2 function key.

**Enter**: The symbol for the Enter (Return) key is ↵. When you see this symbol, press the Enter key.

**Click**: Most mice have two or more buttons. The expression *click the mouse* means to press and release either the left or right button. The middle button, if present, is never used.

**Click and Drag**: This is the process of positioning the mouse arrow in a selected location, pressing the left button, and moving the mouse while holding the button down. You do this to position components and to view and select from pull-down menus.

**Cursor**: This is the flashing object on your screen. The mouse location is shown by the arrow. When you click the mouse, the cursor position moves to the mouse arrow location.

**Select**: Item selection is done with the mouse by moving the mouse arrow to the item and clicking the left mouse button. It is done with the keyboard by pressing the Tab key until the flashing cursor is at the desired item, and then pressing the space bar. Selected items are highlighted.

**Keyboard**: A mouse is preferred, and instructions in this book are given for mouse users. Keyboard users can perform most functions with a few simple keystrokes. For example, pull-down menus are accessed using the first letter of the menu name. Items within the menu are selected by typing the corresponding number. Some common instructions can be accessed with a single keystroke. For example, the F2 function key runs the simulation. These keystrokes are indicated in the pull-down menus.

Although the manual is addressed to mouse users, we refer to some keystrokes in the first section to help those without mice to get started. Sometimes the keystrokes are more convenient than the mouse steps (for example, pulling down the appropriate menu and selecting *Run* probably takes more time than pressing the F2 function key). In such cases the choice is emphasized in the manual.

A summary of all keystroke instructions is included in Part III, Chapter 2 of this manual.

# 2

## Initializing and Installing the Student Edition of MICRO-CAP IV

This chapter leads you through the steps you must follow before using the Student Edition of MICRO-CAP IV: preparing disks, making backup copies of the original disks, and installing MICRO-CAP IV so it works with your equipment.

You need the following items:

- The disks that came with the MICRO-CAP IV program
- The DOS system disk or DOS installed on your hard disk
- An IBM PC, XT, AT, PS/2 or compatible system with a floppy disk drive and a hard disk

## Working with Disks

Although we assume that you are already somewhat familiar with the basic operation of your computer, we begin by emphasizing some important points to keep in mind when you work with disks:

- Do not touch the exposed areas of the disk. If you are using a 3½-inch disk, do not handle it with the shutter (the sliding metal door at the bottom center of the disk) open.

- If you are using 5¼-inch disk, take care when you write on the disk label; a sharp point or hard pressure may damage the disk. Use a felt-tip pen to write on a label that is already on the disk.

- Always place the 5¼-inch disk back in the sleeve after use.

- Keep any disk away from heat, sunlight, smoke, and magnetic fields, such as telephones, televisions, and transformers.

- Do not remove a disk while the drive access light is on.

## Starting Your Computer

Before you can make copies of your MICRO-CAP IV disks, you must load DOS, the disk operating system that lets the computer do basic tasks such as copying and formatting disks. Your computer should be off when you start this section.

1. Turn on the computer.

2. Enter the date (if necessary) in the form MM-DD-YY and press ↵.

3. Enter the time (if necessary) in HH:MM 24-hour format and press ↵.

When you have finished entering the date and time, the operating system prompt appears. This manual uses C> for the hard disk drive; your prompt may look somewhat different.

## Installing MICRO-CAP IV

Installation of the software is straightforward. Switch to drive A by typing **A:**. You now have the prompt A>. Place the original program disk into drive A and type

**INSTALL C:\MC4S** ↵

The suggested directory is MC4S, but you can choose any directory name. Simply substitute that directory name for MC4S in the above command. The Install program decompresses files and copies them to the directory you choose. It also copies circuit and library files to a subdirectory called DATA.

## Starting the Program

Before you run the main program, you must enable your mouse. This is done by executing the MOUSE.COM program (or an equivalent routine from your mouse system software). In many cases this program is executed as part of the AUTOEXEC.BAT file.

Now you are ready to start the program. Switch to the MC4S subdirectory (unless you chose a different name during the installation). Then type

**MC4S** ⏎

Command-line parameters can be specified as part of running the program if you want to force the program to run in a particular mode. As an example, you can have the program run in a lower resolution mode if you experience problems with your graphic card. The graphics mode can be set to override the mode determined by MICRO-CAP IV by appending the following commands to the command line:

| | |
|---|---|
| **/C** | CGA mode, 640X200 resolution, 2-color |
| **/M** | MCGA mode, 640X480 resolution, 2-color |
| **/H** | Hercules mode, 720X348 resolution |
| **/E** | EGA mode, 640X350 resolution, 16-color |
| **/V** | VGS mode, 640X480 resolution, 16-color |
| **/SV** | Super VGA mode, 800X600 resolution, 16-color |
| **/XV** | Extended VGS mode, 1024X768 resolution, 16-color |

For example, to run in the lowest-resolution CGA mode, at the DOS prompt you type

**MC4S/C** ↵

In normal operation it should not be necessary for you to add the graphics command, as MICRO-CAP IV automatically selects the highest resolution available on your computer.

There are two versions of the program on your disk. When you execute MC4S, the program first checks to see whether or not you have a co-processor, and then executes the appropriate program. The simulations will run slower if you do not have a co-processor. The title page will tell you which version has been selected. One line on that page will either read "Student Coprocessor Version" or "Student Non-coprocessor Version". You can force the program to run either the co-processor version or the non co-processor version by executing MC4C or MC4E respectively. MC4E will run on any machine, while MC4C will only run on a machine with a co-processor.

You now are ready to use this powerful simulation tool. However, before going any further we strongly recommend that you do two things: configure the program for your printer and select the proper data directory path.

To configure the program for your printer, pull down the **Options** menu at the top of the screen and select *5:Printer setup for text*. This produces the **Text setup** window, as shown in Figure 1.

You then tell MICRO-CAP IV what type of printer you are using. You can also select whether you want to send text output to parallel ports, serial ports, the screen, or a file. For most cases you would choose *Screen*. Once you configure the program for your printer, you need not do it again unless you prematurely terminate this run of the program or you change printers. Press the Esc key to leave this setup window.

You should also set up your printer for graphics by selecting *6:Printer setup for graphics* from the **Options** pull-down menu and then selecting your printer, the port to which your printer is connected, and the number of dots per inch (for LaserJet printers). If you are using a dot matrix printer, you

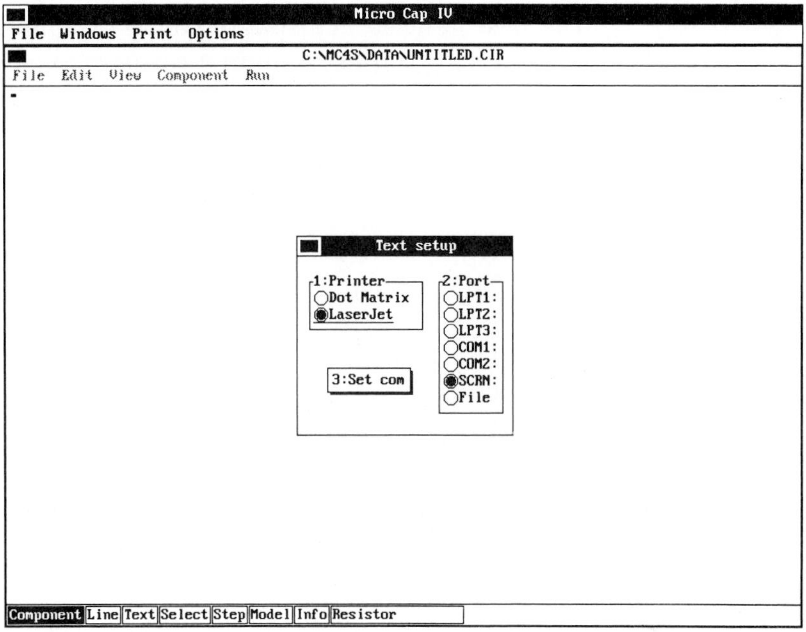

Figure 1

notice that there are two other entries, **Dot Matrix 1** and **Dot Matrix 2**. Your selection between these two depends on the manner in which your printer deals with pixels (that is, whether it considers pixels square or round). Since this information is not readily available in most printer manuals, we recommend you first try **Dot Matrix 1**. If your printed graphics appear distorted, then switch to **Dot Matrix 2**.

The same process is used to set up plotter parameters. In each case you can select communications settings. You normally use default values for these, but you can customize if your plotter or printer manual contains suggestions.

The second thing you should do when you first run the program is tell it where to find DATA files, which include circuit files (we have supplied many example schematics) and libraries that describe component models (such as the 2N2222 transistor). When you run the installation program, the files are placed in a subdirectory of the main directory. For example, if you use a main directory called C:\MC4S in the installation, the files will be copied to a subdirectory called C:\MC4S\FILES. The default file path for the program is C:\MC4S\FILES. When you run a program, MICRO-CAP IV looks for files in the MC4S\DATA subdirectory.

If you have installed the program into a directory other than MC4S, then the program, by default, looks for files in the main directory. Therefore, for your program to be able to find DATA files, you should change the directory path now. Pull down the **File** menu (the one at the upper-left corner of the main window) and select *5:Change data path*. This presents you with a Directory dialog box. At the top of this box, you should see C:\MC4S\DATA\, which indicates the current path. You need to change MC4S to the directory name you chose for the installation. You can accomplish this by cycling through directories (that is, choose [..], then [..] again, then [NAME], and then [DATA]). Alternatively, you can simply go to the line at the bottom of the dialog box (using your mouse or pressing the Tab key until the cursor moves to the bottom) and type

**C:\NAME\DATA\**

where NAME is the directory name you chose. Then press ↵ or type **2**, or use the mouse to select *2:Done.* The top of the dialog box should now read C:\NAME\DATA\. When you properly exit the program, this data path is stored, so you should not have to change it. Of course, if you wish to load or save circuit files to a different directory or to a floppy disk, you would have to make a change at that time.

You also need to tell the program where to look for the library that contains models of the devices used in your circuit. These include components such as the 2N2222 transistor and the 741 op-amp. These models are in a file called SMALL.LBR, which the installation program has copied to the DATA subdirectory of the directory in which you installed MICRO-CAP IV. In more advanced applications, you may want a variety of model libraries for different applications. The program automatically looks for the library stored as C:\MC4S\DATA\SMALL.LBR. If you have selected a different directory than MC4S, you need to tell the program to load the library from that directory. You need do this only once, since the path is memorized when you exit the program.

Pull down the **Windows** menu and select *2:Model Editor*. This opens the **Model Editor** window. We describe that window in Tutorial #1, when you learn to enter devices with parameters from the library. For now, concentrate on the title box. When you first install MICRO-CAP IV, the title box should read C:\MC4S\DATA\SMALL.LBR. If you have installed your program in a directory other than MC4S, you must change the path to the appropriate directory. Do this by pulling down the **File** menu that is part of the **Model Editor** window. Then select *2:Load library*. This presents you with a Directory dialog box. At the top of this box, you should see C:\MC4S\DATA\SMALL.LBR, which indicates the current path. You want to change MC4S to the directory name you chose for the installation (we call this NAME). You can accomplish this by cycling through directories (that is, choose [..], then [..] again, then [NAME], then [DATA], then [SMALL.LBR]). Alternatively, you can simply go to the line at the bottom of the dialog box (selecting with your mouse or pressing the Tab key until the cursor moves to the bottom), and type

**C:\NAME\DATA\SMALL.LBR**

Then press ↵ or type **2**, or use the mouse to select *2:Done.* The top of the dialog box should now read C:\NAME\DATA\ SMALL.LBR. To exit this window, press the Esc key.

## Leaving the Program

You will learn how to exit the program when we discuss the menus in the first tutorial. In the meantime we want to give you at least one way to exit from the keyboard in case you cannot wait for that section of the manual (for example, if you get an important phone call and must turn off the computer now, or if you forgot to load your mouse software). You can clear any window by pressing the **Esc** key. Then press the F3 function key. The program asks you to confirm that you want to exit, and you simply type **Y** for yes. You have now left MICRO-CAP IV.

## A Word About Windows

MICRO-CAP IV operates by the use of windows. If you have not used a windows environment program before, you will be learning some of the standard rules as you use this program. Most windows contain one or more menus that present a list of commands of the same type. Some menus have submenus.

You select menus with the mouse by clicking on the menu name. In many cases the commands available in menus are assigned hotkeys, which make command selection quicker. If a command has a hotkey, the key combination is displayed to the right of the menu command.

All windows have standard features. For example, you can change window sizes, move windows, or close windows by activating certain items in the menu bar at the top of the window. We describe these common features in Tutorial #1. If you are already familiar with windows, this material will serve as a review for you.

# 3

# Introduction to the Student Edition

Now that you have installed the software, you are ready to explore the power of this simulation program.

There are two radically different approaches toward learning to use a piece of software. One is to read a manual and then approach the computer and hope you remember most of what you read. The second is to sit down at the computer and learn as you go along. Fortunately MICRO-CAP IV is sufficiently user-friendly that you can take the second approach. The only possible damage you can do is to erase a portion of the files. Since you have not yet created your own files, such damage is easily correctable by reinstalling the software. Therefore, we encourage you to experiment. Learn what each instruction does by reading the manual and then trying it on the computer.

Another feature of MICRO-CAP IV that simplifies learning by doing is the context-sensitive help screens available in each menu. Any time you need more information before completing a task, you can press the F1 function key (or pull down the appropriate menu and select **Help**). If you do this before running a simulation, you get a help index that allows you to select the topic in which you are interested. If you call for help at some stage of a simulation, the help screen provides information relative to the operation you are performing.

We begin our study by whetting your appetite with a simple example. You will be running a simulation within the next ten minutes. The tutorials in Part II take you through the formal steps of using this software. That is not the purpose of this section, however. Our purpose here is to motivate and excite you and, perhaps, to encourage the more adventurous among you to rely less upon this manual and more upon learning by experimentation.

## An Easy Example

Although you probably have purchased this program to analyze complex active electronic circuits, we illustrate its simplicity of use and its power with a simple passive circuit analysis. In this example you analyze the RLC circuit shown in Figure 2, where the source is a pulse of height 5 volts and duration 400 nanoseconds (nsec).

You perform three types of analysis on this circuit. First, you find the output voltage time function, $v_{out}(t)$. Second, you plot the frequency response of the circuit (that is, the complex transfer function). Finally you perform a dc analysis and plot the output voltage versus input voltage under dc steady-state conditions.

Before you can do any analysis, however, you must draw the circuit. MICRO-CAP IV has one of the easiest interactive drawing systems of any circuit analysis program. Instead of having to lay out the entire circuit in advance and feed it into the computer using node numbers (as in SPICE), you actually draw the circuit on the monitor, component by component. As easy as this is, it still requires practice, and you will become adept at it only by experimenting and learning from your mistakes. The basics of element drawing can be learned in about five minutes.

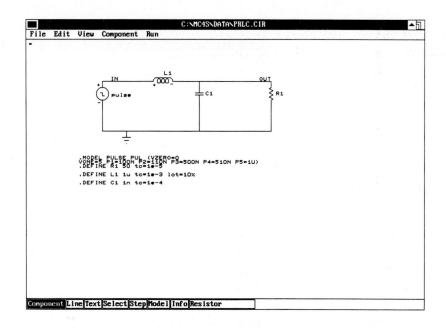

Figure 2

## Retrieving the Circuit

Permit us a caution that should be obvious: This manual is not meant as bedside reading. You should be sitting at your computer as you read the next few pages. You will learn the details of drawing circuits in Tutorial #1. Since this RLC circuit has already been drawn for you and is stored on the disk, we will not take the time to redraw it at this point.

You begin by executing the MICRO-CAP IV program. To do so, switch to the proper directory (MC4S, unless you chose something different during installation), and then type

**MC4S** ↵

to run the program. Your screen should now look like Figure 3.

The screen contains two menu bars. The top one is the main menu bar, consisting of the options **File**, **Windows**, **Print** and **Options**. The box in its upper-left-hand corner is called the system window box. This is described later in this manual. You also have a drawing window containing an

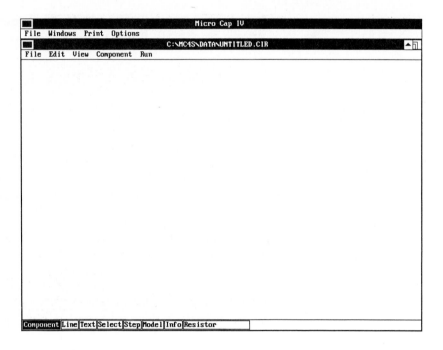

Figure 3

untitled circuit. This second window contains a circuit window menu bar consisting of the options **File**, **Edit**, **View**, **Component**, and **Run**. Since at this time you are not drawing the circuit, but are calling it from memory, begin by clearing this untitled circuit. Pull down the **File** menu that is part of the circuit window (the lower of the two **File** menus), and you will find that your first choice allows you to unload the default untitled circuit. Select this using the mouse. If you prefer to use the keyboard, select the menu by typing the first letter of its name, and then select the menu entry by typing its corresponding number. Thus, you would type

**F; 1**

Once you do so, the front window clears, and your monitor looks like Figure 4.

Figure 4

You now want to load the file from the disk. Pull down the **File** menu and select *3:Load Schematic* to load a circuit file. Keyboard users type

**F;3**

The contents of the data directory are displayed. Use the mouse or the arrow keys to scroll down, and select PRLC.CIR by clicking on it or by pressing ↵. You can jump to the first entry starting with P by typing **P**. This loads the circuit from the disk, and your screen should now look like Figure 2.

MICRO-CAP IV automatically numbers the nodes for you. In specifying which variables you want to plot, you must know these node numbers. Display the numbers by pulling down the **View** menu and selecting *4:Show Node Numbers*. The equivalent keystrokes should be obvious by now (**V;4**), so we will stop indicating them. Now the screen looks like Figure 5.

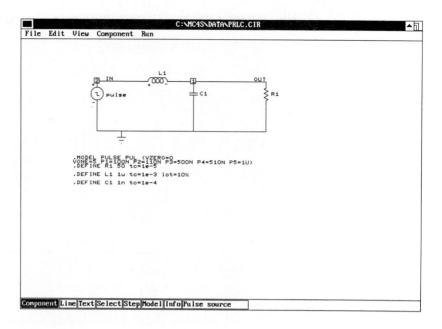

Figure 5

Note that there are two nodes (in addition to ground), and these have been numbered 1 and 2. The .MODEL and .DE-FINE statements under the circuit schematic provide the program with details regarding the component values and the pulse source. We cover this in detail later in this manual.

## Transient Analysis

The first type of analysis you perform is the transient analysis. This plots specific time waveforms. Pull down the **Run** menu and select *1:Transient analysis*. This displays the **Transient Analysis Limits** window shown in Figure 6.

As this window is currently configured, the results of the simulation will be in the form of four different time plots. These are the voltages at nodes 1 and 2, the voltage difference between nodes 1 and 2, and the voltage difference between nodes 2 and 1. For now, don't be concerned with the fifth line, which selects the current in the capacitor.

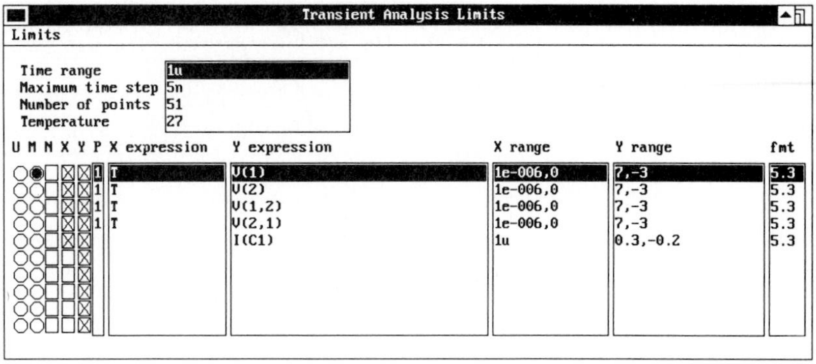

Figure 6

Since we are not currently going to change anything in the **Transient Analysis Limits** window, simply press the F2 function key to run the simulation (alternatively, you can close this window by pressing the Esc key and then pulling down the **Transient** menu and selecting *1:Run*). The result is shown in Figure 7.

Although this manual is printed in black ink, we hope you have a color monitor and can see that multiple colors have been used to differentiate the four curves. Suppose you decide that the graph is too cluttered, and you want to display only the two node voltages. To do so, pull down the **Transient** menu and select *2:Limits*. This places you back in the **Transient Analysis Limits** window. Clear the 1 from the P column for the third and fourth plots. Simply position the cursor at each 1 using the mouse and then delete it (with the **Delete** key), or replace it with a space. The modified limits window is shown in Figure 8.

Before rerunning the simulation, you can do one additional thing to make the outputs more distinguishable. Clear the **Transient Analysis Limits** window by pressing the Esc key. Then pull down the **Transient** menu again, select *3:Options*, and on the window that appears next, select *T:Tokens* (click on the box to the left of the option name to produce an X). This window is shown in Figure 9.

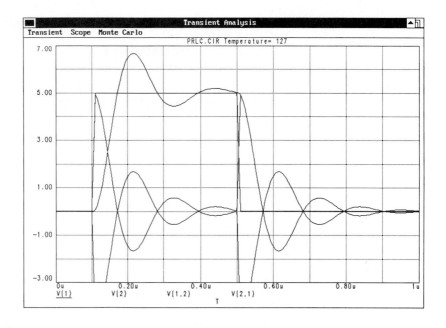

Figure 7

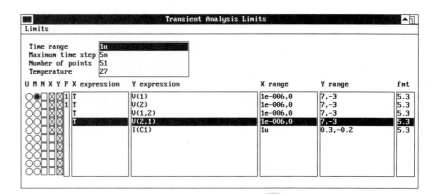

Figure 8

The use of tokens distinguishes the curves from each other. Even before you rerun the simulation with the changes that you have made, tokens are immediately added to the existing curves as soon as the option is selected. Now press the F2 function key to run the simulation. The result looks like

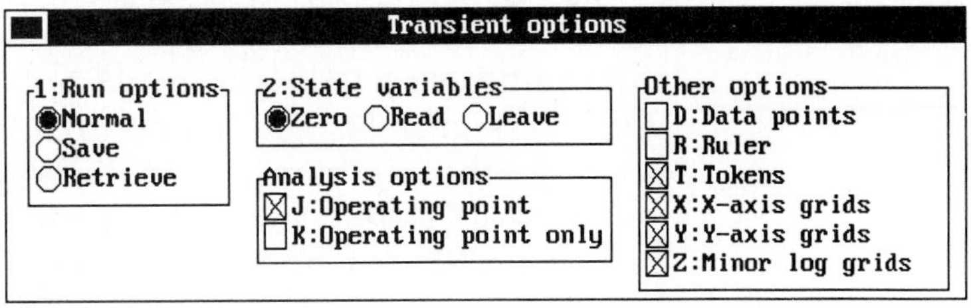

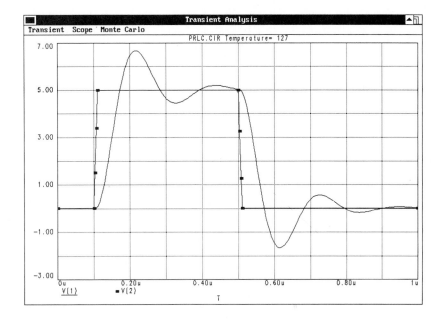

Figure 9

Figure 10

Figure 10. This simulation is much less cluttered than your first one. Note that V(2) is marked with solid square tokens. Had there been more than two curves, additional distinguishable tokens would be displayed on the other curves.

Suppose you want to know the peaks of the overshoot. The **Scope** menu allows you to position up to two cursors to read specific values. Pull down the **Scope** menu and select *2:Cursor Mode*. Position one cursor at the peak and click the left mouse button. Position a second cursor at the minimum value using the right mouse button. The result is shown in Figure 11. You can now read the maximum as 6.663 and the minimum as –1.665. We positioned these cursors "by eye," so they may not exactly match what you get. Later you will see how to locate these points automatically.

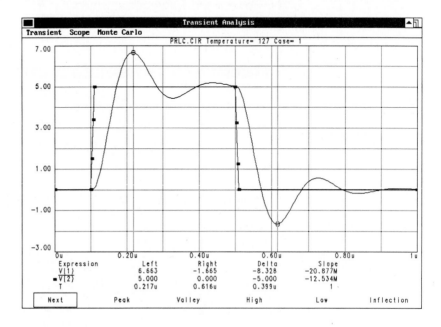

Figure 11

Before leaving the transient analysis, you can do one more thing: explore the stepping process. Pull down the **Transient** menu and select *4:Stepping*. You then see the **Stepping** window, shown as Figure 12. You can see we have made changes from what is stored on your disk. You can make these changes by positioning the cursor, clicking the left mouse button, and then entering the text you want followed by ↵.

What we have displayed in this menu is a request to step the resistor value, R1, from 10 ohms to 50 ohms in linear steps of

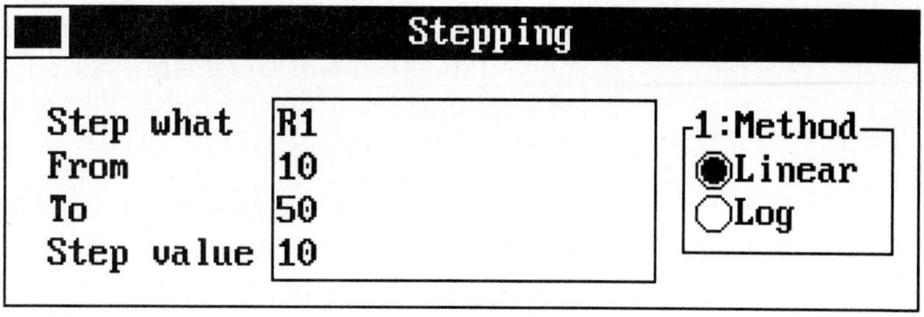

**Stepping**

| | | | |
|---|---|---|---|
| Step what | R1 | | ┌1:Method┐ |
| From | 10 | | ●Linear |
| To | 50 | | ○Log |
| Step value | 10 | | |

Figure 12

10 ohms. The simulation therefore runs five times, using resistor values of 10, 20, 30, 40, and 50 ohms.

Now press the F2 function key to run the simulation. The result is shown in Figure 13.

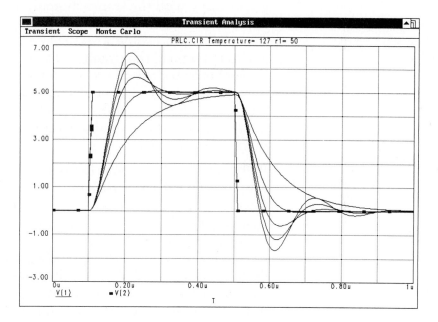

Figure 13

As the simulation runs, you can see the resistor values displayed at the top of the graph. Note that the curves go from overdamped to underdamped. You will learn later how to add labels to the curves.

Congratulations! You have run your first simulation. To exit the simulation, either pull down the window box at the upper-left of the front window (the solid box above the **Transient** pull-down menu) and select *6:Exit analysis*, or simply press the **F3** function key.

## AC Analysis

Now let's perform a frequency analysis on this same RLC circuit. In ac analysis you plot output as a function of frequency. The straight-line approximation to this plot is the familiar Bode plot. The ac analysis is run in a manner similar to that of the transient analysis. If you have just finished experimenting with the transient analysis, you already have the RLC circuit loaded into the computer. However, rather than simply proceeding with the ac analysis, we are going to ask you to unload the circuit and then reload it. The reason we do this is to clear all the operations you entered during the transient analysis. For example, the last thing you did was to step the value of the resistor. If you were to proceed immediately to the ac analysis, the program would continue in the stepping mode.

Pull down the **File** menu that is part of the **Schematic Editor** window and select *1:Unload circuit*. Before unloading the RLC circuit, the program will ask you if you want to save changes. You do not want to save the stepping instructions, so answer no by typing **N** or clicking on **No**. Then pull down the main **File** menu and select *3:Load schematic*. Scroll down to the PRLC.CIR entry and press ↵. This loads the RLC circuit with its original menu entries. Now you can initiate the ac analysis by using the mouse to pull down the **Run** menu and select the *3:AC analysis* entry.

For the ac analysis we assume sinusoidal inputs and steady-state operation. Initiation of the analysis presents the **AC Analysis Limits** menu, as shown in Figure 14.

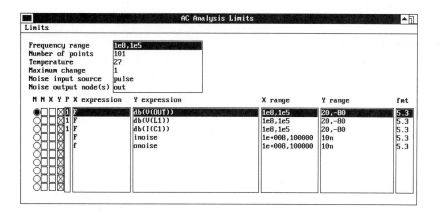

Figure 14

You again choose the default values stored in the example. These entries create three plots: the output voltage, the voltage across the inductor, and the current through the capacitor. Each curve is in decibels, with frequency ranging from 100 kHz (1E5) to 100 MHz (1E8). The ordinate ranges from −80 to +20 dB. Since the curves are distinguished by different colors, and our printer only prints one color, we do as we did with transient analysis and place tokens on the curves. To do so, close the **AC Analysis Limits** window (press the Esc key, or pull down the window box in the upper-left-hand corner of the window), then pull down the **AC** window and select *3:Options*. Finally, select *Tokens* (click on this entry so there is an X in the box). Run the analysis by first clearing the **AC options** window (by pressing the Esc key) and then pulling down the **AC** menu and selecting *1:Run*, or by simply pressing the **F2** function key. The analysis then proceeds and generates curves as shown in Figure 15. Note that the output voltage amplitude plot starts at 0 dB for low frequency and approaches a slope of -40 dB/decade as the theory predicts.

As in the case of transient analysis, we can step any parameter to create a family of curves. Suppose, for example, you want to step the resistor from 10 ohms to 50 ohms. We use the **AC** menu to select *4:Stepping*, and enter the same

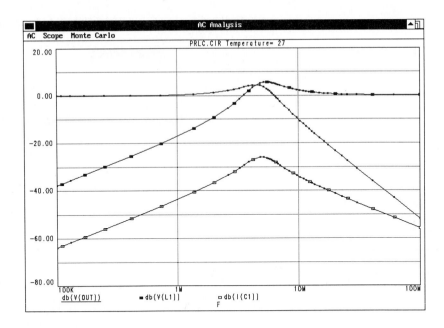

Figure 15

parameters as in the transient case (see Figure 12). This creates a series of five sets of curves, thus cluttering the diagram with 15 curves. You can simplify the diagram by eliminating two of the original three plots and simply view the output voltage. To do this, clear the **Stepping** window by pressing the Esc key, pull down the **AC** menu, select *2:Limits*, and then remove the ones from the P column for the second and third plots. This produces the plot of Figure 16.

We once again exit the analysis either from the pull-down window box (select *6:Exit analysis*) or by pressing the F3 function key.

## DC Analysis

DC analysis plots output versus input under dc conditions. Ideal capacitors become open circuits, and ideal inductors become short circuits. The dc analysis is run in the same manner as the transient and ac analyses. Although you have already drawn the circuit, we once again ask you to unload

Figure 16

this circuit and then reload from the disk. This is necessary to clear the changes you have made (such as stepping). Unload the circuit from the **File** menu, and then load the new PRLC circuit following the earlier instructions. Initiate the analysis by using the mouse to pull down the **Run** menu and select the *3:DC analysis* entry.

Initiation of the analysis presents a **DC Analysis Limits** menu, as shown in Figure 17. We again choose the default values, which plot V(2) versus V(1). The input voltage ranges from 0 to 10 volts. We initiate the simulation either by clearing the **DC Analysis Limits** menu (pressing the Esc key), pulling down the **DC** menu and selecting *1:Run*, or pressing the F2 function key. The analysis generates the curve shown in Figure 18.

Note that the input/output characteristic is a straight line of unity slope. This result is not surprising since, under dc conditions, the capacitor is an open circuit and the inductor is a short circuit. Thus, the output voltage equals the input

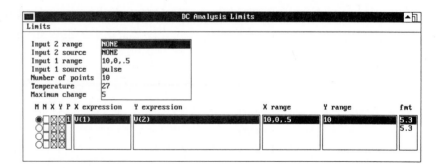

Figure 17

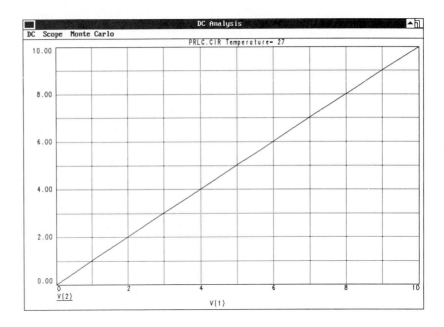

Figure 18

voltage. The dc analysis mode is more interesting when non-linear devices are present in the circuit.

You can exit the analysis by either pulling down the window box menu and selecting *6:Exit Analysis*, or by pressing the F3 function key.

We have illustrated the three circuit analysis options for a simple example. Even though the circuit you analyzed did not contain any nonlinear passive devices or any active electronic devices, we hope you can sense the excitement and tremendous power of this program.

The only things we have not covered in this simple example is how to draw your own circuit and some of the more subtle features of the program, such as Probe and Monte Carlo analysis. You may wish to stop at this point and experiment with the program using the stored circuits. The worst damage you can cause by experimenting is to erase a file from the disk. Since you have not yet created any of your own circuits, you can always reinstall the program. So go ahead, be brave. Learn what the various menu entries do. Experience is an excellent teacher.

The next major section of this manual takes a more detailed approach toward gaining skill with the program by first learning how to draw complex circuits in Tutorial #1. We then explore the three analysis packages in detail. Tutorials #2, #3, and #4 are intended to stand on their own, so you may cover them in any order.

# II

## TUTORIALS

In Part I of this manual we presented an example to whet your appetite. We hope you found that RLC circuit to be both interesting and motivating. Although it introduced you to many features of this powerful software, it did so in the context of solving only one simple circuit.

This portion of the manual contains a detailed presentation of the major features of this program. You can learn to use this software in several ways. One way is to read all of the tutorials and then start doing examples. However, if you are like most of us, you will have forgotten the earlier portions of the chapter by the time you reach the end. A second way is to learn a few features at a time and practice until you are comfortable with them. Yet another way is to start using the software in your course work and learn the various levels of sophistication as you need them. This method proves best for the majority of students. Many of the most complex features of the program may be of limited use to you, so the only purpose in reading about them now is to be aware that they are available, in case you need them at a later date.

To close the loop and receive feedback in your learning attempts, we recommend that you solve the problems at the back of each tutorial. Your instructor has answers to the problems.

# 1

# Schematic Editor

When you run MICRO-CAP IV you immediately enter the Schematic Editor mode, and your screen looks like Figure 19. We begin this tutorial with a brief description of the entries on this screen. Then we illustrate the circuit-drawing process with a simple example. Finally we give a detailed description of the various components and devices available in MICRO-CAP IV.

## The Schematic Editor Screen

**Windows Menu Box**   The **Windows Menu Box** is the small box located in the extreme upper-left-hand corner of the screen. If you select it with your mouse, you are presented with a menu of three items.

> 1:Micro-Cap IV
> 2:Help
> 3:Quit

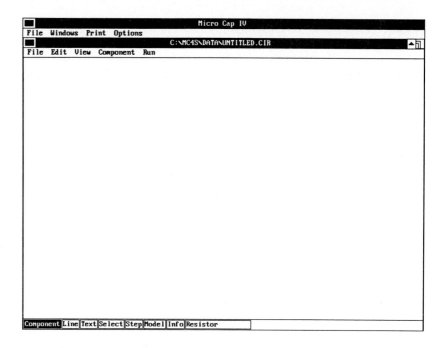

Figure 19

**1:Micro-Cap IV**  Simply displays the date, time, authors, and software revision letter of your version of MICRO-CAP IV.

**2:Help**  Displays a help screen. You can also access help at any time by pressing the F1 function key. If you access it at this early stage, you get overall information on the program operation. If you access it later, you get context-sensitive help. Exit *Help* by pressing the Esc key or clicking on *Cancel* in the window.

**3:Quit**  Select this to exit the software (after confirming the selection in a dialog box). You can also quit an operation at any time by pressing the F3 function key.

**System Menu**

There are four pull-down menus in the **System** menu across the top line of the screen: File, Windows, Print, and Options. We now describe each of these.

## File Menu

This menu provides six selections. Only the first five can be accessed in the Student Version of MICRO-CAP IV.

    1:New schematic
    2:New SPICE file
    3:Load schematic
    4:Load SPICE file
    5:Change data path

**1:New schematic**  Clears the screen before drawing a new schematic.

**2:New SPICE file**  Creates a new SPICE text window. You use it to begin a new SPICE circuit specification.

**3:Load schematic**  Loads a circuit file from disk. When you choose this, you are presented with a file dialog box allowing you to load, erase, or cancel the instruction. You scroll through available files from this box. You can scroll with the mouse or execute some faster forms of control with the keyboard. If you type any alphanumeric key, the cursor moves to the first item that begins with the character you entered. You can also use the up and down arrow keys for scrolling. The page up and page down keys scroll the list one page at a time. If you press Ctrl+Home or Ctrl+End, you move to the first or last item on the list, respectively.

**4:Load SPICE file**  Loads an existing SPICE text file from disk.

**5:Change data path**  Alters the data path for circuit and output files.

## Windows Menu

You can exert some types of window control without having to access this menu. In particular, you can move or resize a window. If you click and drag your mouse in the title bar of the window, you move that window. You can resize a window using the icon containing several sizes of rectangles located to the far right of the title bar. A click and drag operation originating on this icon causes the window outline to track the mouse movement.

The **Windows** pull-down menu provides five functions.

1:Restore windows
2:Model Editor
3:Component Editor
4:Shape Editor
5:Calculator

**1:Restore windows**  If you have altered the window size or placement, this selection restores the windows to their standard size or location (choose *Cascade* to have the windows overlap each other).

**2:Model Editor**  Accesses the Model Editor, which is used to review and edit the device model libraries. For example, you use this editor to enter data on a transistor or op-amp, or to vary current data (for example, the Beta of the 2N222A transistor). We talk about this in more detail later in this tutorial. You will probably make extensive use of this editor.

**3:Component Editor**  Accesses the Component Editor, which manages the general component types that can be placed in a circuit. These include resistor, diode, and NPN transistor.

**4:Shape Editor**  This editor maintains the graphical shapes used to represent components in a schematic. For example, if you want to change the symbol for a resistor from a jagged series of lines to a square (although we cannot imagine why you would want to do this), you use this editor.

**5:Calculator**  Accesses the expression calculator. It lets you enter a mathematical expression. When you press Enter (⏎) the numerical result is displayed.

At the bottom of the **Windows** pull-down menu is the name of the window(s) currently open.

## Print Menu

This pull-down menu presents you with three print options.

1:Print front window graphics
2:Print front window text
3:Print entire screen

**1:Print front window graphics**  Produces a graphics printout of the contents of the front, or selected, window.

**2:Print front window text**  Produces a SPICE text printout of the contents of the front, or selected, window.

**3:Print entire screen**  Prints a graphics image of everything you see on the screen. We have used it to create many of the figures in this manual.

## Options Menu

This pull-down menu presents seven choices.

1:Palette
2:Preferences
3:Global settings
4:Plotter setup
5:Printer setup for text
6:Printer setup for graphics
7:Schematic print/plot options

**1:Palette**  Allows you to control display colors.

**2:Preferences**  Provides for specification of eight preferences.

**1:Mouse ratio**  High or low ratio of mouse movement to arrow movement.

**2:Sound**  Enables or disables sound in warnings and error messages.

**3:File warning**  Enables or disables use of warning message when circuit has been changed.

**4:Directory dialog**  Enables or disables file dialog box.

**5:Quit warning**  Causes system to ask for exit verification before quitting.

**6:Floating nodes**  Checks circuit for floating nodes (connected to only one component) prior to analysis.

**7:Pivot solver**  Usually disabled, this routine is needed in some ac analyses.

**8: Node snap**  When enabled, components are adjusted so pins coincide with the nearest circuit component that is within two grids.

**3:Global settings**  Allows you to set the values for various numeric constants used in the simulation.

**4:Plotter Setup**  Provides control over the plotter, including plotter type, paper size, pen settings, and output port. Note that this refers to an actual plotter and not to a printer being used to plot graphics. In many cases users of MICRO-CAP IV do not use plotters, but use printers to produce copies of graphics.

**5:Printer setup for text**  Text or numeric output generated by the program, such as netlists and analysis results, may be sent to a disk file, a window on the screen, or the printer. Printer output may be directed to one of several ports and in dot matrix or HP laser printer format.

**6:Printer setup for graphics**  Printer output of the various graphics may be sent to a disk file or to the printer. Printer output may be directed to one of several ports, and in dot matrix or HP laser printer format.

If you have not yet done this, we suggest that you stop at this point and use options 5 and 6 to set up the program for the printer you are using. If you fail to do this, you may run into trouble when you try to print a circuit or simulation result.

**7:Schematic print/plot options**  Controls schematic output. It lets you specify what to output and the number of pages.

We remind you that if we do not give you all of the details you want relative to a specific topic, you can press the F1 function key at any time. This gives you help that focuses on the portion of the program you are using.

## Pull-Down Menus

This completes our brief description of the menus in the main window of the screen. You can clear any window you have displayed by pressing the Esc key. You should now be back to the display of Figure 19. The **Schematic Editor** window includes a window box in the upper-left-hand corner, a title bar (which currently reads "C:\MC4S\DATA\UNTI-TLED.CIR"), a zoom box (the upward pointing arrow in the upper-right-hand corner), and a size box (to the right of the arrow). Below the title bar are five pull-down menus: **File, Edit, View, Component,** and **Run**. Four of these five menus (**File, Edit, View,** and **Run**) are not used until after a circuit is drawn on the screen. The **File** menu is used to save the circuit. The **Edit** menu is used to edit the circuit during or after drawing. The **View** menu is used to display certain aspects of the circuit or to search for components, parameters, text, or node numbers. The **Run** menu is used to begin the simulation. The **Component** menu is described in detail in the next section.

## Tools Menu

At the bottom of the **Schematic Editor** window is the **Tools** menu consisting of eight entries.

> Component
> Line
> Text
> Select
> Step
> Model
> Info
> Resistor (or currently selected component)

You will learn about each of these as you go through this tutorial.

# Drawing a Circuit

We illustrate the use of the **Schematic Editor** window with a simple example. We draw the circuit of Figure 20, which is essentially the same circuit we analyzed earlier in this manual (PRLC from the file), except that the parameter values have been simplified. That is, if you compare Figure 20 with Figure 2, you find that the only difference is in the specification of passive components.

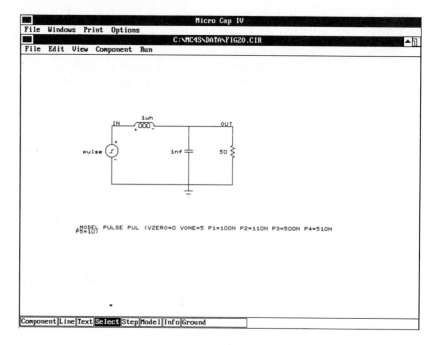

Figure 20

You draw the circuit much as you would with pencil on paper—one component at a time. Your drawing tools are the **Tools** menu at the bottom of the screen and the **Edit** and **Component** pull-down menus at the top.

Begin by drawing the pulse source. Pull down the **Component** menu, and select *E. Pulse Source* (or select *2:Waveform sources* and then *Pulse Source*). Note that after you perform these steps, "Pulse source" appears as the rightmost entry in the **Tools** menu at the bottom of the screen. This display always tells you what is currently selected. Move the mouse arrow to the desired location on the screen and click the left button. If you hold that button down, you can drag the component to any location on the screen. If you click the right button while holding down the left button, you reorient the element into any of four rotations (90 degrees each) and the reflected (mirror-image) versions of these. When you are satisfied with the location and orientation of the pulse source, release the mouse button. You are then presented with a text box in the upper-left corner of the screen. This is where you type the name of the source. We have chosen to call it PULSE, so type:

**PULSE;** ↵

The case does not matter because MICRO-CAP IV does not recognize any difference between upper- and lowercase. You therefore could type **Pulse** or **PULSE** or **pulse** if you prefer.

The screen should now resemble Figure 21. The pulse source appears on the screen as a shadow image until you perform the next operation. The shadow image simply lets you know which part of the drawing is currently selected. This becomes important if you wish to make changes, but we will cover that later.

If you were to reposition the cursor and press the left button again, the program would draw whatever is currently selected (the right display in the **Tools** menu). You do not want to add any more pulse sources, so you need to change that selection. Pull down the **Component** menu, select *Passive components,* and then select *Inductor*. Now draw the inductor in the location you want. When you release the mouse button, you need to type in the value of the inductor. You either could give it a name (such as L1) and then later instruct the program on the specific value, or you could directly enter a value in henries. Type **1uh** (with no spaces) for a 1-microhenry inductor. Then press Enter (↵). Continue this process for the capacitor (select *Passive components* and then *Capacitor*, or use the hotkey C) and resistor (select

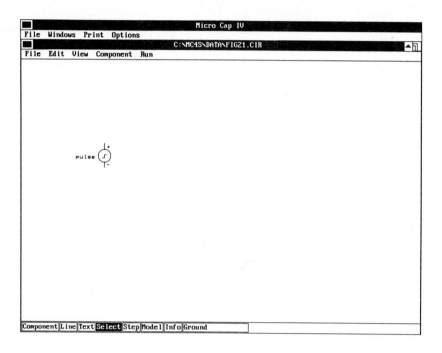

Figure 21

***Passive components*** and then ***Resistor***, or use the hotkey
A). The screen should now resemble Figure 22. The exact
placement of the components is not critical.

Your next job is to connect the components using lines. Select
the ***Line*** entry from the **Tools** menu at the bottom of the
screen. You can either use the mouse to click on this entry, or
simply type **L**. Then, to connect any two points, position the
mouse cursor on the first point, press the left button, and
while holding down that button move to the second point. A
single corner is placed as needed. If you press the right button while holding down the left, the corner shifts to the other
orientation. With the ***Node snap*** option you need not position exactly on a node but simply close to it.

After drawing the lines, the circuit should look like Figure 23.

If you attempted to run a simulation at this point, you would
receive an error statement because you are driving the

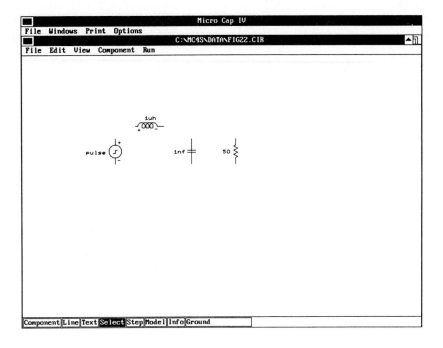

Figure 22

circuit with a source you chose to call PULSE, but the program does not know what this is. You must provide a definition using the .MODEL statement. .MODEL statements are described in detail later in this tutorial. The statement is added by selecting *Text* from the **Tools** menu, positioning the cursor where you wish to add the text (any blank part of screen), pressing the left mouse button, and then typing the following text:

**.MODEL pulse PUL (VZERO=0 VONE=5 P1=100N P2=110N P3=500N P4=510N P5=1U)** ↵

The period in front of the word "MODEL" is critical. The program cannot run without it. This statement defines a pulse source going from 0 volts to 5 volts, starting the leading edge at 100 nsec, reaching 5 volts at 110 nsec, starting the trailing edge at 500 nsec, and reaching 0 volts at 510 nsec.

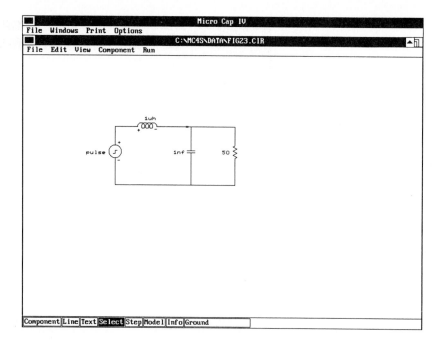

Figure 23

You still are not quite ready to run a simulation. Every circuit you draw on the screen must have a ground, otherwise attempts at analysis result in an error statement. Once you select **Ground** from the **Component** menu (select **G:Ground** or **8:Connectors** and then select **Ground**), you add it to the circuit in the usual way (click the mouse, click and drag to move, click the right button to rotate).

Now you are finished entering the circuit. Your screen should look like Figure 24.

But suppose you make a mistake in drawing the circuit. If the mistake involves simply mislabeling a component, there is no need to erase anything. You simply choose **Select** from the **Tools** menu (click the mouse on the **Select** entry, or type **S).** You then click the mouse on the appropriate component. That component is highlighted in shadow drawing. If you want to move the component, simply click and drag. If you

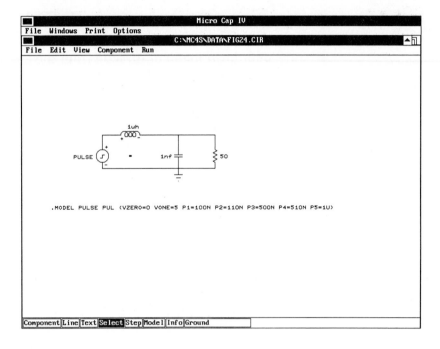

Figure 24

want to change its label or value, double click on the component and then correct the label in the text box in the upper-left-hand corner of the screen. If you want to reorient (for example, rotate), click the right button while holding the left. You may wish to use this reorientation feature to change the location of labels. For example, suppose you have a vertical resistor with the label on the left and that this label is interfering with another label on the diagram. You can rotate the resistor to move the label to the right side.

For more serious changes, you may want to delete a portion of the circuit. You select the portion in one of two ways. If the portion is a component, simply click on the component (while in the select mode). If the portion is a region of the circuit, click and drag to outline a rectangle. In either case, once you have selected the part you want to delete, pull down the **Edit** menu and select *5:Clear*.

If all you wish to do is cancel the previous action, you use the Undo instruction. You can either access this from the **Edit** pull-down menu or directly from the keyboard. From the menu select *1:Undo*. From the keyboard use the hotkey combination Alt+Backspace; that is, you press the Backspace key while holding down the Alt key. This undoes the effect of the last command.

Ordinarily the next step would be to run a simulation. We discuss that in the next three tutorials. The remainder of this tutorial describes all of the drawing features of the program. We know you are anxious to start running simulations, but you need to be aware of the power of the schematic drawing part of the program so you can enter a wide variety of circuits. To follow the steps in the following description, you first should clear the circuit you have just drawn. Do this by pulling down the **File** menu in the second row on the screen (the one that is part of the **Schematic Editor** window), and click on *1:Unload circuit.* The program asks you if you want to save the modified circuit. Click on **No** (or type **N**). This removes the circuit window. We need the **Schematic Editor** window to draw any circuits. To restore it, you pull down the **File** menu and click on *1:New schematic*.

## Component Menu

The pull-down **Component** menu allows you to choose from 18 different selections.

> 0: Passive components
> 1: Active components
> 2: Waveform sources
> 3: Laplace sources
> 4: Function sources
> 5: Dependent sources
> 6: Macros
> 7: Subckts
> 8: Connectors
> 9: Miscellaneous

A: Resistor
B: Battery
C: Capacitor
D: Diode
E: Pulse source
F: Sine source
G: Ground
H: NPN

The ten numbered items represent classifications of components, and we describe each of these in the following sections. The eight lettered choices represent hotkeys. All of these are contained in the ten numbered selections (for example, resistors, capacitors and diodes are part of the passive components list), but the separate listing allows faster selection. In fact, using the keyboard instead of the mouse is often faster. If you are drawing a circuit and want to select *Diodes*, simply type

**C;D**

The first letter selects the **Component** menu, and the second selects the *Diodes* entry. In the case of the battery, capacitor, diode, and ground, it should be easy to remember the associated hotkey—it is the first letter of the element name. You can change any of the hotkey selections you wish. To do so, pull down the **Component** menu, select the appropriate group, and then use the arrow keys to highlight the entry you wish to assign to a hotkey. Then use the Alt key to make the assignment. For example, suppose you wanted hotkey H to select PNP instead of NPN transistors. You highlight PNP by selecting *Active components* from the **Component** menu and then using the arrow key to scroll down to PNP. Then press Alt+H. PNP transistors are now assigned to hotkey H in the **Component** menu.

## Model Editor

Before we discuss the entries in the **Components** Menu, we take a moment to examine the Model Editor. You may need to use this editor to specify properties of certain components.

Diodes, active components, and waveform sources are more complex than the basic elements (resistor, inductor, and capacitor). In the case of elements, the component is specified by a single parameter (that is, ohms, henries, or farads). The more complex devices require more extensive model parameters. The diode requires 15 parameters, while op-amps and transistors require many more parameters to describe the way they behave in a circuit. The Model Editor contains a library of models for the various devices. We discuss the editor configuration for various devices as each device is presented. For now we use the diode library as an introduction to the general characteristics of the Model Editor.

You can create a library of standard diodes. To create a library, enter the Model Editor by pulling down the **Windows** menu and selecting the second entry, ***2:Model Editor***.

The Model Editor layout for the diode is shown in Figure 25.

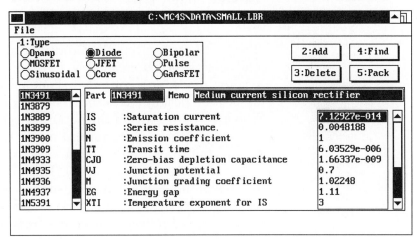

Figure 25

In addition to the typical windows information included in the title box at the top, it consists of four important areas.

The upper-left area allows you to select a type of device. Simply click the mouse on the circle next to the type you wish (for example, *Diode*).

Directly below the type section is a parts list. This scrollable list includes all entries in the current library. A library containing common diodes already exists on your disk. You can add or delete from this list by using the selections in the upper-right-hand corner. Selecting *2:Add* adds a new part to the library. It is added to the bottom of the parts list as "-unnamed-" and with the default parameter values. Selecting *3:Delete* removes the selected part from the library. Selecting *4:Find* searches the library for a specified part name. The *Find* feature is more important in the professional version of the software where the model libraries contain over 3000 parts. For the size of the Student Version libraries, it is probably more convenient to scroll through the list. Selecting *5:Pack* deletes duplicate or unnamed parts (down to a minimum of two entries).

The largest area of the **Model Editor** window contains the actual model parameters. The part has a name and an optional memo. Then each of the model parameters is listed. You can change any item by using the mouse to position the cursor at the item and typing the new entry. Updates to the library are automatically saved when you close this window. There is no need to use the pull-down **File** menu unless you want to create multiple libraries.

Note that the initial diode library contains many common diodes. The 15 SPICE 2G.6 diode model parameters are loaded with the appropriate values derived from manufacturers' data sheets. These parameters and the default values are discussed in Part III of this manual. You can find out what the default values are directly from the program. Simply add an "-unnamed-" diode to the library. It will automatically be loaded with the default values for the parameters. The diode library we have supplied usually will be sufficient for your applications, but as you become more sophisticated, you may want to expand this library to include specific diode parameters from manufacturers' data sheets. The **Model Editor** library window is closed by pulling down the window box in the upper-left-hand corner of that window and selecting *6:Close*, or simply by pressing the Esc key.

## Passive Components

This selection in the **Component** menu allows you to choose from a list that includes

> Resistor
> Capacitor
> Inductor
> Lines (transmission line)
> Diode (Diode, D45 and Schottky)
> Transformer

**Resistors, capacitors,** and **inductors** are handled in a similar manner. You make your selection from the menu and then draw the element by clicking the left mouse button. If you hold this button down, you can drag the component to any desired location on the screen. If you click the right button while still holding the left, you reorient (rotate or reflect) the element. After placing the item in the circuit, you must use the keyboard to enter the number of ohms, farads, or henries. You can enter these numbers in one of three separate formats:

- **Real numbers**  Enter the value of the component. For example, 1 megohm would be 1000000 and 1 microfarad would be .000001.

- **Floating point (Scientific notation)**  Enter a number using powers of 10. For example, 1 megohm is entered as **1E6** and 1 microfarad by **1E-6**.

- **Engineering notation**  Use the following abbreviations for power of 10.

| | | |
|---|---|---|
| F | Femto | 1E-15 |
| P | Pico | 1E-12 |
| N | Nano | 1E-9 |
| U | Micro | 1E-6 |
| M | Milli | 1E-3 |
| K | Kilo | 1E3 |
| MEG | Mega | 1E6 |
| G | Giga | 1E9 |
| T | Tera | 1E12 |

Thus 1 megohm could be entered as **1MEG** or **1000K**. You may also add unit designations after the abbreviation without affecting the value. Do not, however, enter F by itself; 1F is $10^{-15}$ (Femto) rather than 1 farad. One microfarad can be entered as **1UF**, **1000NF**, or **10E-6F**. In each case, the **F** can be dropped. Do not leave any space between the numeric and the abbreviation.

A second way to specify the value of a passive component is to give the component a name and then to use the .DEFINE statement. For example, when prompted for the resistor value in the previous example, instead of simply entering **50**, you could name the component. For example, you could type

**R1** ⏎

Then in any blank part of the diagram, you would enter text (select **Text** from the **Tools** menu, position the cursor where you want to add the text, click the left mouse button, and then type the message) for the .DEFINE statement in the form,

**.DEFINE R1 50** ⏎

The period in front of the word "DEFINE" is critical. The case is not critical. You would accomplish the same operation by typing

**.Define r1 50** ⏎

Within this definition you can use a number of mathematical operations and symbols. For example, you can include tolerances for components. These become important in Monte Carlo analysis. The statement

**.DEFINE R1 50 lot=10%** ⏎

defines a resistor of 50 ohms with a tolerance of ±5 ohms.

When we discuss the Stepping operation (which we experimented with in the simple example of the previous section), we will see that in order to step a component value, the component must be labeled. For example, if the resistor were simply entered as 50 ohms, there would be no way to identify it for stepping. This is one justification for using .DEFINE statements.

You have three choices for entering diodes in your circuit. You can select ***Diodes*** for a junction diode, ***D45*** for a junction diode drawn at a 45-degree angle, and ***Schottky*** for a Schottky diode. If you select one of the types of diode and then add this component to your drawing, you next have to enter the diode designation. You should give the diode a name. If you are not in a creative mood, you can use the name D1. If you do so, the next diode you add will have a default label of D2. Alternatively, if you label the first diode as M1, the default for the next diode will be M2.

On your circuit drawing, if you labeled your diode D1, you need a .MODEL statement to tell the program the parameters of D1. If you want to define D1 as one of the entries in your model library, you use a .DEFINE statement. Suppose, for example, you have a library entry with a part name of 1N3491, and this is what you wish D1 to be. You could have entered this label directly on the schematic while drawing the element, but since you did not, you must enter the following .DEFINE statement using the Text mode. Select any blank area of the screen and type

**.DEFINE D1 1N3491** ⏎

You will still need a .MODEL statement for the 1N3491, but you don't need to type it yourself, as we discuss in the next section.

Alternatively, you can devise your own .MODEL statement and select any parameters you want to vary from default values. For example, if you type

**.MODEL D1 D(IS=1P CJO=1P TT=1N TOL=50%)** ↵

you are specifying default parameters except for a saturation current (IS) of 1 picoampere, a zero-bias junction capacitance (CJO) of 1 picofarad, and a transit time (TT) of 1 nanosecond. If you want D1 to have default values for all parameters, you can type the following .MODEL statement:

**.MODEL D1 D()** ↵

or you can let MICRO-CAP IV supply the statement. You also can include a tolerance in the .MODEL statement, and you have chosen to do so above. This tolerance is used in Monte Carlo analysis.

If you click the *Line* entry on the **Passive components** menu (*not* the **Tools** menu), you add a transmission line to the diagram. You must specify the characteristic impedance of the line and the line length. Line length is defined by specifying either the delay through the line or both the frequency and the number of wavelengths. You also should give the transmission line a name (for example, T1). A typical specification would be given by typing

**T1 ZO=75 TD=5n** ↵

which specifies a characteristic impedance of 75 ohms and a delay of 5 nanoseconds. Alternatively, a line might be specified as

**T1 ZO=150 F=125Meg NL=0.5** ↵

In this case the characteristic impedance is 150 ohms, the frequency is 125 MHz and the line is 0.5 wavelength long.

The *Transformer* option from the **Passive components** menu inserts a four-terminal transformer model consisting of two inductors with a mutual inductance between them. When prompted for a keyboard entry after drawing the transformer, you need to enter three numbers: the primary inductance, the secondary inductance, and the coefficient of coupling. For example, if you enter

**.01,.0001, .98** ↵

you are specifying a transformer with primary inductance of 10 millihenries, secondary inductance of 0.1 millihenry, and a coefficient of coupling of 98%.

### Generating .MODEL Statements from the Tools Menu

Each source, active component, line, diode, and transformer *must* have a .MODEL statement appearing on the schematic. Otherwise you receive an error statement when you try to run the program. Even if you have used a component from the library (for example, a 1N3491 diode), the .MODEL statement for this device must appear on the schematic. MICRO-CAP IV automatically generates these statements if you click the ***Model*** entry on the **Tools** menu (or type **M**). MICRO-CAP IV then searches your schematic for each component that requires a .MODEL statement. If it finds a component for which a .MODEL statement is not already on the diagram, the program first checks whether the item name is in the Model Editor library (for example, the 1N3491 diode). In such cases MICRO-CAP IV copies the parameters from the library to a .MODEL statement which it places on the schematic. If you have not typed a .MODEL statement nor used a device from the library, MICRO-CAP IV adds a .MODEL statement using default parameters.

When you invoke the ***Model*** command from the **Tools** menu, MICRO-CAP IV prints the required .MODEL statement at the cursor location. If MICRO-CAP IV detects more than one device that requires a .MODEL statement, these may be printed on top of each other on the screen. While this does not affect the program execution, you may wish to keep the statements separated for easy reading. To do so, invoke the ***Model*** command after entering each device that requires a .MODEL statement. Place each statement where you want it by positioning the cursor before printing the statement, or by clicking and dragging after it is printed.

## Active Components

When you select this item from the **Component** menu, you are presented with a second menu containing 12 entries, as follows:

NPN
PNP
NPN4
PNP4
NMOS
PMOS
DNMOS
DPMOS
NJFET
PJFET
Opamp
GaAsFET

When you click the desired component, you have selected that component for addition to the circuit. The selected item appears in the right-hand entry of the **Tools** menu at the bottom of the screen. You add the item to the circuit in the same way you did for passive components: Press the left mouse button, and drag the item to the correct position. While holding the left button, click the right button to reorient (rotate or reflect) the component.

Once you enter the component on the diagram, you must type a description. A box appears in the upper-left-hand portion of the screen for this purpose. To the right of the box is a + sign. If you click on that sign, you are presented with the entries in the model library. Clicking one of the entries names the component for that particular library entry. An alternative is to give the component a name and then use either a .DEFINE statement to set the component to an entry in the library or a .MODEL statement to define the parameters of the component.

### *NPN* and *PNP*

Once you add either of these bipolar junction transistors to your circuit, you can select items from the model library by clicking on the + sign. The bipolar model library comes loaded with many standard transistors. If you cannot find a transistor you want to use, you can add one to the library.

Alternatively, you can define your own parameters using the .MODEL statement.

Suppose you decide to name your transistor Q1. If you then decide that Q1 should be a 2N2222A general-purpose transistor (which is an entry in the model library), you enter the following text in any clear portion of the screen:

**.DEFINE Q1 2N2222A** ↵

Then you can have MICRO-CAP IV copy the .MODEL statement from the library by selecting *Model* from the **Tools** menu (or by typing **M**). If you did not wish to use a transistor in the model library, you could use the .MODEL statement to define any parameters that differ from the default values. The model used by MICRO-CAP IV (the SPICE model) contains 40 parameters. You can view these parameters on screen in the model library (access them from the *Model Editor* selection in the **Windows** pull-down menu). Figure 26 shows one bipolar entry from the library, the 2N2222A general-purpose transistor.

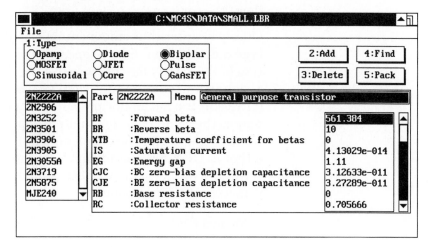

Figure 26

When you add an "-unnamed-" item to the model library, you see the default values for the parameters. As an example, the default value for the forward beta (BF) is 100. Suppose you want your transistor, which you named Q1, to be an NPN transistor with the default parameter values except for the saturation current (IS), forward beta (BF), and reverse transit time (TR). You type a .MODEL statement of the form

**.MODEL Q1 NPN(IS=1E-15 BF=55 TR=.5N) ⏎**

We have set the saturation current to $10^{-15}$ amperes, the forward beta to 55, and the transit time to 0.5 nanosecond. The other 37 parameters are set to default values.

*NPN4* and *PNP4* are four-terminal versions of the basic junction transistors. The additional terminal is the *Substrate*.

### NMOS, DNMOS, PMOS, and DPMOS

The letter "D" stands for "discrete," while the absence of a "D" indicates an integrated circuit MOS transistor. The appropriate symbols appear on the screen when you add any of these active devices to your circuit. The library for MOSFETs contains standard entries. Figure 27 shows one entry from the model library for MOSFETs.

The instructions for adding these devices are identical to those of the bipolar transistors. The MOSFET model used by MICRO-CAP IV is specified by 52 parameters. Of these, 42 are from the original SPICE 2G.6 model. You can read the parameters on screen from the model library. The LEVEL parameter can be one of three values, with 16 of the parameters not used in the level 1 model. The more complicated the model, the more accurate the results, but the slower the simulation.

You use the .MODEL statement in the same manner as for other active devices.

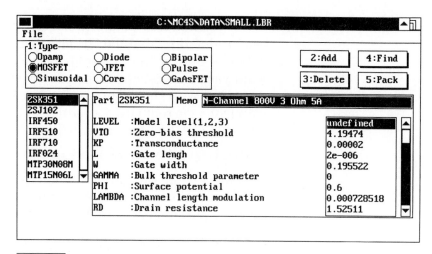

Figure 27

## *NJFET* and *PJFET*

Adding either type of JFET is done in the same manner as other active devices. The library of JFETs contains standard entries. Figure 28 shows one entry from this library.

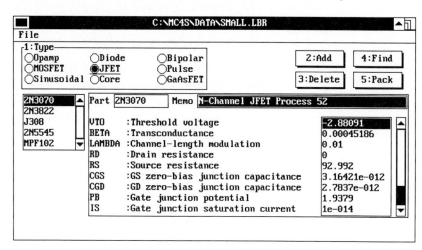

Figure 28

The JFET model is specified with 12 parameters. If you don't want to select a device from the library, you can use a .MODEL statement to define those parameters that differ from default values. Suppose, for example, you add a JFET and call it J1. You want this to be an NJFET with default parameters except for a threshold voltage of 0.2 volts, a transconductance of $10^{-4}$, and a channel-length modulation of 0.001. You type the following .MODEL statement at any blank part of the screen:

**.MODEL J1 NJF (VTO=.2 BETA=1E-4 LAMBDA=1E-3)** ↵

## *OP-AMPS*

You add an op-amp in the same manner as other active devices. The op-amp model library contains a variety of common devices. Figure 29 shows one entry from this library.

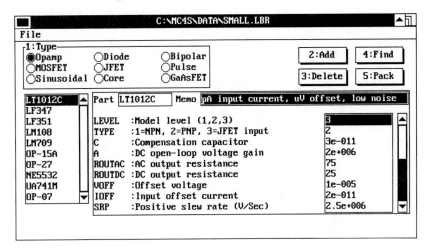

Figure 29

The model used by MICRO-CAP IV is specified with 20 parameters. The first of these is the model level, which can take on one of three values. The second parameter describes the op-amp type: NPN, PNP or JFET. The remaining 18 parameters describe the operation. For level 1 models, only three of the operational parameters are used. This represents a simple voltage-controlled current source with a finite output resistance and open loop gain. Level 2 adds another four parameters to this list and is a three-stage, two-pole model with slew rate limiting, finite gain, and output resistance. Level 3 is an enhanced Boyle model similar to those implemented in other SPICE programs as subcircuits. It uses all 18 operational parameters.

If you don't want to select an op-amp from the library, you can use a .MODEL statement, as we have with other devices. Suppose, for example, you name an op-amp A1 and want it to have default parameters except for a DC open-loop gain of 45,000, an input offset voltage of 0.002, a maximum positive slew rate of 250,000 and a unity gain bandwidth of 1 MHz. You type the following .MODEL statement at any blank portion of the screen:

**.MODEL A1 OPA(A=45K VOFF=.002 SRP=250K GBW=1E6)** ⏎

### GaAsFETs

Gallium Arsenide n-channel FET devices are capable of much higher speeds than devices fabricated using silicon. The MESFET is an example of this type of device. The GaAsFET model used by MICRO-CAP IV (SPICE 2G.6 has no model for the GaAsFET) contains 22 parameters. You can view these in the model library. Figure 30 shows an example of one entry in this library.

The first parameter specifies one of two possible model levels. All parameters, with the exception of the doping tail extender, B, are used by both models. The library contains no specific parts—only two default entries (Default1 and Default2). You must either add entries to the library or use a .MODEL statement to define those parameters different from the default values. You can see from the library entries that 11 of the parameters default to zero.

If you don't want to select a GaAsFET from the library, you can use a .MODEL statement, as we have with other devices. Suppose that you enter a device on the schematic and name

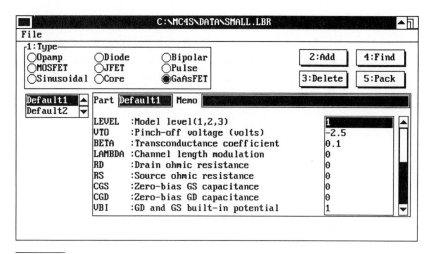

Figure 30

it B1. You want this to be a GaAsFET with default parameters except for a pinch-off voltage of –2, a transconductance coefficient of $10^{-4}$, and a channel length modulation of 0.001/volt. You would type the following .MODEL statement at any blank portion of the screen:

**.MODEL B1 GASFET (VTO=-2 BETA=1E-4 LAMBDA=1E-3)** ↵

## Waveform Sources

When you select this item from the **Component** menu, you are presented with another menu containing seven entries which are discussed in the following sections.

Battery
Pulse Source
ISource
User Source
Sine Source
V
I

**Battery**

If you select *Battery* and then enter the component on the schematic, you are prompted for the battery voltage. You can enter a value or give the battery a symbol and specify its value with a .DEFINE statement. For example, if you label the battery as V1, you can then define the value, say 6 volts, by typing the following at any blank portion of the screen:

**.DEFINE V1 6** ↵

**Pulse Source**

If you select ***Pulse Source*** and then enter the component on the schematic, you are presented with a dialog box where you either type a label or click on the + to display the model library entries. The model library comes with several pre-loaded entries. We urge you to explore the entries in this library (from the Model Editor) so you know what is available. The names should give you a hint of the waveshape. Figure 31 shows an example of one entry in this library.

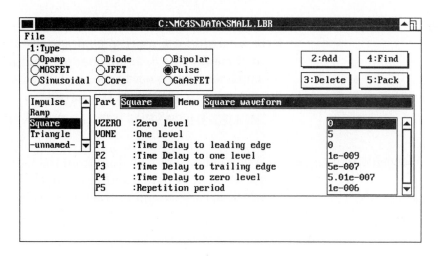

Figure 31

The pulse source produces a waveform as shown in Figure 32. The waveform is specified by seven parameters. You can learn the default values by adding one entry to the library.

**VZERO**  The zero level, or the initial value of the waveform in volts. The default value is zero.

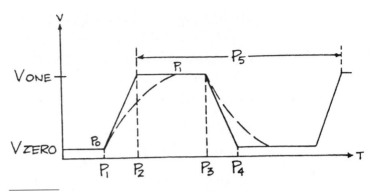

Figure 32

**VONE**  The one level, or the pulse height in volts. This parameter models the high level of the waveform, and the default value is 5.0 volts.

**P1**  The delay time in seconds. This parameter models the time delay from time equals zero to the leading edge of the waveform. It can be any nonnegative value, including zero. The default value is 1.0E–7 seconds, or 0.1 μs.

**P2**  The time delay to the one level, that is, the time at which the high value is reached. The rise time is the difference between P2 and P1. Default value for P2 is 1.1E–7, yielding a rise time of 10 ns. You can create an infinite slope by setting P2 equal to P1.

**P3**  The time delay to the start of the trailing edge. Its default value is 5.0E–7, or 0.5 μs.

**P4**  The time at which the low value is reached. The fall time is the difference between P4 and P3. Default value for P4 is 5.1E–7, yielding a decay time of 10 ns.

**P5**  The period of the waveform. Default value is 1.0E–6, or 1 μs.

If you do not want to use a source from the library, you can use a .MODEL statement, as we did in the simple example at the beginning of this tutorial. In that example, we labeled the source PULSE and typed the following .MODEL statement on a blank portion of the screen:

**.MODEL pulse PUL(VZERO=0 VONE=5 P1=100N P2=110N P3=500N P4=510N P5=1U)** ⏎

This defines a 5-volt pulse with rising edge between 100 and 110 nanoseconds and trailing edge between 500 and 510 nanoseconds. The period is 1 microsecond. Since each of these is the default value, we could have omitted them from the .MODEL statement and simply typed

**.MODEL pulse PUL ()** ⏎

Alternatively, we could have let MICRO-CAP IV type the .MODEL statement by selecting *Model* from the **Tools** menu.

### Isource

*Isource* is a DC current source. You specify the value after drawing the source on the screen in the standard manner.

### User Source

The *User Source* is a voltage source that gets its values from a user-defined file in an ASCII text file. This file contains N sequential values representing the waveform at N successive timepoints. The extension of the file name must be .USR. The file may be created using a text editor, by external software, or by saving a waveform from a transient run to a user file Source (you will learn to do this in the next tutorial).

### Sine Source

The *Sine Source* is an independent voltage source defined by seven parameters. Once you add this to the schematic, you must type a label or description. When you click on the + sign, you are presented with the model library. Figure 33 shows an example of an entry in this library.

The library currently contains a sampling of sources. You can add to the library depending on your applications and requirements. The parameters allow you to set frequency (in Hz), amplitude, dc offset level, phase shift (in radians), source resistance, exponential time constant (for decaying

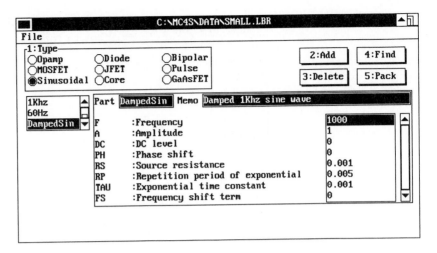

Figure 33

amplitudes), and repetition period of the exponential. Figure 34 shows a simple example of a sinusoid, where the parameters we have chosen are the default values of amplitude (1 volt), frequency (1 MHz) and source resistance (1 milliohm), a dc offset level of 1 volt, an exponential time constant of 2 microseconds, and a repetition period of 10 microseconds. The figure was generated from the simple circuit of Figure 35. All we did was display the node voltage by performing a transient analysis (Tutorial #2 teaches you to run a transient analysis—you must first add a ground).

### V and I

These are ***independent sources.*** You can specify pulse, sinusoid, exponential, tabular, or frequency modulated waveform. In addition, you can specify an ac source with a given magnitude and phase for use in ac analysis. We see an example of this type of ac source when we find the ac input impedance of the TL3.CIR transmission line circuit in the examples of **Tutorial #3**.

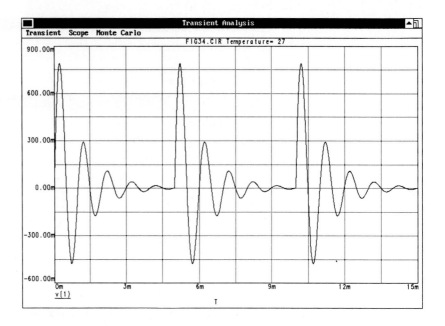

Figure 34

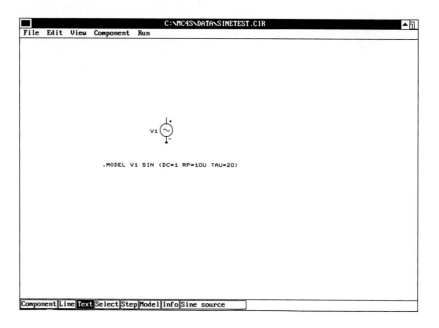

Figure 35

The **ac source** specification is given by labeling the current or voltage source

**AC magval [phaseval]**

where **magval** is the magnitude and **phaseval** is the phase. If the phase is omitted, it defaults to zero.

The **pulse source** specification is

**PULSE v1 v2 [td [tr [tf [pw[per]]]]]**

where **v1** is the initial value, **v2** is the pulse value, **td** is the delay, **tr** is the rise time, **tf** is the fall time, **pw** is the pulse width, and **per** is the period. Figure 36 shows an example of the waveform generated from an independent voltage source with the specification

**PULSE .4 1.6 .1u .1u .2u .1u .5u**

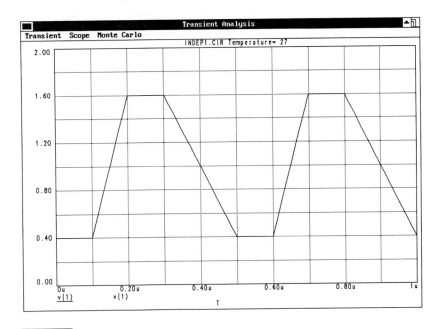

Figure 36

The **sinusoidal source** specification is given by labeling the current or voltage source

**SIN vo va [freq [td [df]]]**

where **vo** is the offset value, **va** is the peak amplitude, **freq** is the frequency, **td** is the delay, and **df** is the dampling factor. Figure 37 shows an example of the waveform generated from an independent voltage source with the specification

**SIN 1 1 10Meg 1 10n 200n**

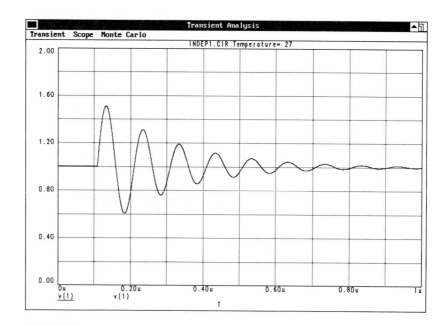

Figure 37

The *exponential source* specification is given by labeling the current or voltage source

**EXP v1 v2 [td [tc1 [td2 [tc2]]]]**

where **v1** is the initial value, **v2** is the peak value, **td1** is the rise delay, **tc1** is the rise time constant, **td2** is the fall delay, and **tc2** is the fall time constant. Figure 38 shows an example of the waveform generated from an independent voltage source with the specification

**EXP 1 2 150n 50n 550n 100n**

The *frequency modulated waveform source* specification is given by labeling the current or voltage source

Figure 38

**SFFM vo va freq [mi [fm]]**

where **vo** is the offset value, **va** is the peak vamplitude, **freq** is the carrier frequency, **mi** is the modulation index, and **fm** is the modulation frequency. Figure 39 shows an example of the waveform generated from an independent voltage source with the specification

**SFFM 2 1 8Meg 4 1Meg**

## Laplace Sources

The fourth entry in the **Component** pull-down menu is *Laplace source*. When you select this item, you are presented with another menu containing eight entries, each beginning with "L" for Laplace.

    LFIofV
    LFIofI
    LFVofV
    LFVofI
    LTIofV
    LTIofI

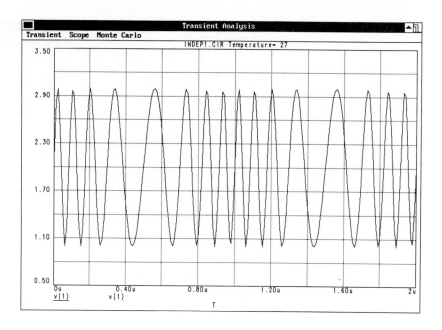

Figure 39

LTVofV
LTVofI

These represent controlled sources where the source and the controlling variable can be either voltage or current. This yields four possible combinations (for example, voltage-controlled voltage source, current-controlled voltage source). Each of the four possibilities has two types of sources: those specified by a formula and those specified by a table. The formula sources contain an "F" in the specification, while the tabular sources contain a "T." Thus, for example, **LFIofV** is a formula-controlled current source controlled by a voltage.

The formula sources can be used to simulate a transfer function. For example, if you specify the formula (after adding the **LFVofV** source to the diagram) as 1/(1+.001*s), your controlled source acts as a first-order low-pass filter with 3-dB cutoff frequency at 1000 radians/sec (159 Hz). Figure 40 shows the circuit for this function and the frequency response plot that results. Note that we have a sinusoidal source, where we have specified default parameters by

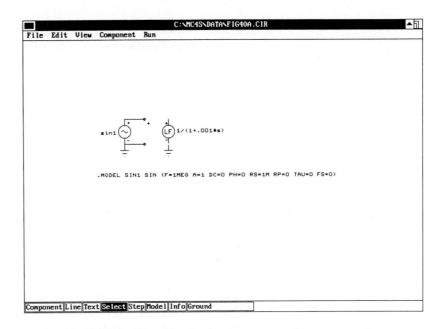

Figure 40

letting MICRO-CAP IV create the .MODEL statement (using *Model* from the **Tools** menu). The plot was produced using the AC analysis program, which is described in Tutorial #3.

If you select a tabular source, you must specify that source in the form of a table. The table must contain ordered triplets of numbers: frequency, magnitude, and phase. You would specify the source with a list of the form

**(F1,M1,P1) (F2,M2,P2) .... (FN,MN,PN)**

The frequency is in hertz. The sets of parentheses must be separated by spaces, and the frequencies must be in ascending order. The program interpolates between points, and for all frequencies below F1, the values are set at M1 and P1. For frequencies above FN, the values are constant at MN and PN. You enter this table either directly when prompted for the parameter value (after adding the source to your figure) or by using a .DEFINE statement. To use the .DEFINE statement, give the source any name you want, and then type a statement of the form

**.DEFINE NAME (F1,M1,P1) (F2,M2,P2) ... (FN,MN,PN)** ⏎

## Function Sources

The fifth entry in the **Component** pull-down menu is the *Function source*. When you select this item, you are presented with another menu containing six entries.

NFV
NFI
NTVofI
NTIofI
NTIofV
NTVofV

The function source can be specified either by an algebraic formula (NF) or by a table of values (NT).

### Formulas

The formula type function source uses an algebraic formula to compute the value of the output variable as a function of any set of time-domain variables. The source can be either current or voltage, designated as NFI or NFV, respectively.

The available functions are summarized below:

**P(X,Y,Z)**  Power flowing into a circuit section. X, Y, and Z are nodes. There must be a resistor or inductor between nodes X and Y. This is needed to measure the current. The current is multiplied by the voltage drop between nodes Y and Z.

**E(X,Y,Z)**  Energy flowing into a circuit section.

**T**  Transient analysis simulation time

**F**  Real AC analysis frequency value (in Hz.)

**S**  Complex radian frequency = $2\pi jF$

**+**  Addition

**–**  Subtraction

**\***  Multiplication

**/**  Division

**MOD**  Modulus

**SIN(x)**  Sine function (x in radians)

**COS(x)**  Cosine function (x in radians)

**TAN(x)**  Tangent function (x in radians)

**ATN(x)**  Arc tangent function

**SINH(x)**  Hyperbolic sine

**COSH(x)**  Hyperbolic cosine

**TANH(x)**  Hyperbolic tangent

**COTH(x)**  Hyperbolic cotangent

**LN(x)**  Natural log

**LOG(x)**  Base 10 log

**EXP(x)**  $e^x$

**ABS(x)**  Absolute value

**DB(x)**  Decibels

**D(x)**  Delta, or change. A derivative can be formed as a ratio of two deltas. For example, D(Y)/D(T) is the numerical time derivative of Y.

**SQRT(x)**  Square root

**SGN(x)**  +1 if x>0, −1 if x<0, −1 if x=0

**^**  Exponentiation operator

**NOT**  Negation operator

**AND**  AND operator

**OR**  OR operator

**XOR**  Exclusive OR operator

The following relational operators are available. They return 1.0 if true, 0.0 if false.

   <  Less than

   >  Greater than

   < =  Less than or equal to

   > =  Greater than or equal to

   <>  Not equal to

   **=**  Equal to operator

Function sources can be used in place of some other active sources we have already discussed. For example, the function voltage source of Figure 41 is a form of sine source.

## Tables

The table type of function source uses a table of ordered data pairs that describe the output variable as a function solely of the input variable. This permits you to simulate complex non-linear input-output relationships. The table describes a transfer function. The input variable may be

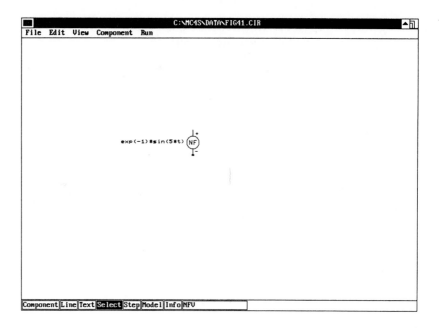

File  Edit  View  Component  Run

exp(-1)*sin(5*t)  (NF)

Component Line Text Select Step Model Info NFV

Figure 41

- a current flowing into the positive input lead
- a voltage between the positive and negative input leads

There are four types of table sources. These are current-controlled current sources (NTIOFI), current-controlled voltage sources (NTVOFI), voltage-controlled voltage sources (NTVOFV), and voltage-controlled current sources (NTIOFV). Once you enter the source on the diagram, you must type in the table. The format is

**(x1,y1) (x2,y2) (x3,y3) ... (xk,yk)**

There are two rules for constructing the table pairs in the source parameter:

1. Values are separated by commas, and pairs are enclosed in parentheses and separated by spaces.

2. Data pairs must be arranged in input ascending order: x1<x2<...xk.

In calculating functions from table pairs, MICRO-CAP IV uses three rules:

1. The output value is constant at y1 for input values below x1.

2. The output value is constant at yk for input values above xk.

3. Output values are interpolated for input values between table entries.

The circuit T1.CIR, which is stored on your disk, is an example of a table source.

**Dependent Sources**   When you select *Dependent Sources* from the **Component** menu, you are presented with eight choices.

IofV
IofI
Vof I
VofV
HVOFI
GIOFV
FIOFI
EVOFV

The first four are conventional dependent sources. If you add one of these to the diagram, you are prompted to enter the proportionality constant for that source. For example, if you select *VofV* and enter **5**, the controlled source voltage is five times the voltage at the input nodes.

The last four entries (preceded by E, F, G, and H) are SPICE polynomial-dependent sources. We will not give details of this type of source in this manual. However, if you are familiar with the SPICE device statements, the conversion to MICRO-CAP IV is simple. The syntax is identical, with the following two exceptions:

1. The "plusout" and "minusout" node numbers are not used in MICRO-CAP IV.

2. All source names referenced must be preceded with an @ symbol.

## Macros

A macro is a circuit containing components, text, and lines. You use macros when a particular circuit configuration is repeatedly used in a larger network. When you select *Macro* from the **Component** menu, you are presented with another menu listing the macros that are preloaded in MICRO-CAP IV, for example, sum, logic blocks (such as AND, and NOR), absolute value, and multiplier. When you add a macro to a circuit, you are actually adding the expanded circuit. Since the simulation uses the expanded circuit, you must be careful not to exceed the 50-node limit of the MICRO-CAP IV Student Edition.

Defining a macro consists of five steps:

1. Create a circuit that defines the contents you want in the macro.

2. Add text labels at the circuit points that connect with the outer circuit. For example, if your macro has three leads, you define these three points using **.PinN**, where N varies from 1 to 3.

3. Add a .PARAMETERS statement to indicate any parameters that the main circuit should request. For example, if your macro contains a resistor R1 and a capacitor C2, and you want to specify these in your main circuit, you need the following statement in the macro:

   **.PARAMETERS(R1,C2)**

   Then the name of the macro in the main circuit would be NAME(R1,C2) where NAME is the name you have assigned to the macro, and R1 and C2 are the appropriate numerical values.

4. Save the circuit in a disk file.

5. Add a new entry in the component library by selecting *2:Add new component* from the **Edit** pull-down menu in the **Component Editor** window. You must specify

- the macro name (the same name used to save it to disk)
- the name of the shape to be used when drawing the macro (you can pick any shape stored in the program)
- a definition type: MACRO
- parameter text locations
- pin assignments

At this point, the macro is available for use in another circuit. To use it, select **6:Macros** from the **Component** pull-down menu, then select the particular macro and place it in your circuit by clicking the left mouse button. When the parameter is requested, you see the selected name there already. If parameters are needed, you must add a list of them in parentheses.

As an example, suppose you want to include an integrator into your circuits at many points. You decide to create a macro to do this. The macro could be as shown in Figure 42.

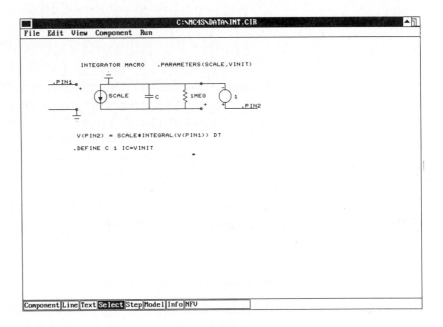

Figure 42

We are using a macro already stored in your program. You can retrieve the schematic at this time using the **3:Load schematic** selection from the **File** pull down menu.

Note that we have used a dependent voltage-controlled current source with proportionality factor SCALE. This feeds a 1 farad capacitor, so the output voltage is SCALE times the integral of the input voltage. We have also provided for an initial condition (charge on the capacitor). We have labeled the two leads .PIN1 and .PIN2, and included a .PARAMETERS(SCALE, VINIT) statement to indicate that the proportionality factor and the initial capacitor voltage are included in the macro name in the main circuit.

We now show an example of the use of a macro. We build a simple integrator using the INT macro. We begin by drawing the circuit of Figure 43.

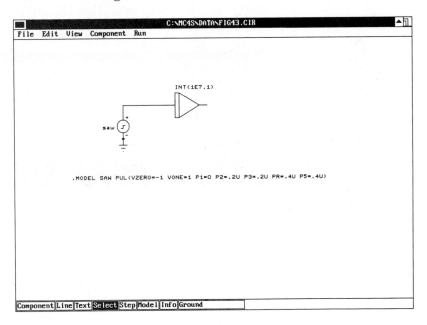

Figure 43

Begin drawing the integrator by selecting **Macro** from the **Component** menu, and then selecting **INT** from the menu of selections. Although the "INT" label appears as a default after you add the component, you must add the two parameters to the label as shown. These indicate that the scale factor we are using is $10^7$ and the initial condition is 1 volt. While you have the integrator macro selected (see the right-hand entry in the **Tools** menu at the bottom of the screen), try pulling down the **Component** menu. You will see how this macro was defined when it was first entered into the program.

The source in the figure is a pulse source from the **_Waveform sources_** menu in the **Component** window. We labeled it "saw" since the parameters specified in the .MODEL statement make this into a sawtooth (sometimes known as triangular) generator.

Figure 44 shows the input and output waveforms (you will learn to generate this in the next tutorial). The output is the integral of the sawtooth. It is shifted to +1 volt because of the initial condition we specified.

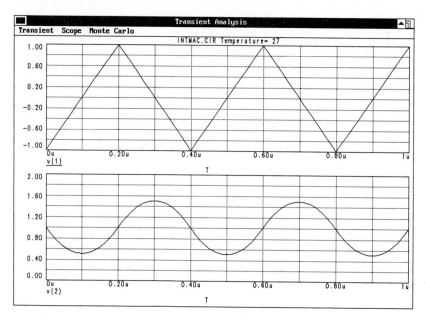

Figure 44

## Subcircuits

Subcircuits are complete SPICE text file circuits, created and saved on disk to be used by other circuits. Their usefulness is similar to that of macros, since a complex circuit block can be incorporated into a larger circuit and it is represented by a single component on the schematic. Many manufacturers create SPICE subcircuit models for their parts, so you can incorporate complex models of real devices into your circuits.

We will not discuss details of subcircuits in this manual. If you want to see what a typical subcircuit looks like, pull down the main **File** window, select *4:Load SPICE file*, and then select the file named UA741.MOD. The screen shows the SPICE listing for a standard Boyle-type model for the UA741 op-amp.

You can create your own subcircuit files with the MICRO-CAP IV SPICE text editor (which we discuss at the end of this tutorial), or by using an external word processor. You can frequently obtain this as a text file from the manufacturer of the device.

## Connectors

When you click the **Connectors** entry in the **Component** menu, you are presented with another menu with 13 entries.

Ground
Tie
Jumper
Jumper 2
Short 1
Short 2
Short 3
Short 4
Short 5
Short 6
Short 12
Short diag
jumdiag1

These selections fall into four categories: ground, short, jumper, and tie.

### Ground

This entry is used to draw a ground. If you hold down the left button, you can drag the ground around the screen to any desired position. While holding down the left button, you can reorient the ground by clicking the right button. Every circuit must have a ground before you run a simulation.

### Short

We have already seen a simple way for drawing lines. Simply select *Line* from the **Tools** menu (either with the mouse or by typing **L**), and then use the mouse to draw the line. However, sometimes you must draw short lines to separate components from each other (that is, add leads to a component). You can use this menu to select any one of seven possible shorts, where the number indicates the length of the short in number of grids.

### Tie and Jumper

When two lines cross in a drawing, it is assumed that a connection exists between the two lines. It would therefore appear to be necessary to make a two-dimensional drawing of the circuit without any intersecting lines (unless they are to be connected). As circuits become more complex, it is not possible to make such a planar drawing. We need ways to cross lines without an electrical connection. The *Tie* and *Jumper* menu selections permit this.

*Jumper* is used whenever lines that are not electrically connected intersect. You add this component and position the loop to lie over the second line. Two different-length jumpers for horizontal or vertical placement in the circuit and one for diagonal placement are available.

Sometimes points that are widely separated must be electrically connected. We could do this by drawing lines connecting the points, using jumpers when necessary. However, this may clutter the diagram unnecessarily. The *Tie* selection provides a simple alternative. You use it to mark the two points with any identical label. They are then electrically tied together. You position the arrow over one of the points and click the mouse. You then type in the label. You repeat the operation for the second point. You can do this for any number of points. An example is shown in Figure 45, where we have used both a jumper and a tie. We have displayed node numbers so you can see that both points having ties labeled A are considered the same node.

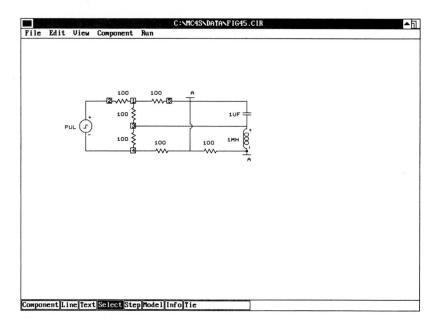

Figure 45

**Miscellaneous**

When you select this entry in the **Component** menu, you are presented with a second menu containing four entries.

Switch
Arrow
Bubble1
Bubble2

When you select *Switch* and draw this on your circuit, you note that the symbol includes a switch and two controlling nodes, as shown in Figure 46. The switch is a four-terminal device.

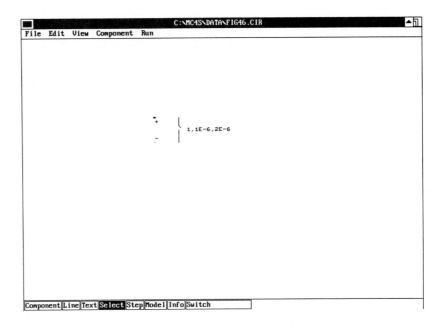

Figure 46

Three types of switches can be used in circuits: current-controlled, voltage-controlled, and time-controlled. If you use a current-controlled switch, you must insert an inductor across the input nodes of the switch. Voltage-controlled switches are controlled by the voltage across the two input nodes, while time-dependent switches use the time variable. In all cases the open switch is represented by a high resistance, ROFF, while the closed switch is represented by a low resistance, RON.

Switches are used only in transient analysis. After you draw a switch, you are prompted to type in the value. This is done in the following format:

**S,N1,N2**

S is the controlling parameter. Type **I** for current-controlled switches, **V** for voltage-controlled, and **T** for time-controlled. N1 and N2 are the threshold values of the controlled parameter between which the switch changes state. You can simulate either a normally open or normally closed switch, depending on whether N1>N2 or N2>N1. If N2>N1, the switch is normally open, and it closes when the parameter is between N1 and N2. If N1>N2, the switch is normally closed, and it opens when the parameter is between N1 and N2.

The *Arrow* and *Bubble* entries in the **Miscellaneous** menu are included to illustrate that you can define a variety of shapes to suit your particular applications. These particular shapes are included as drawing tools to make your circuit diagrams more complete. The arrow can be used to label nodes or wires in the circuit, and the bubble is used to enhance diagrams (for example, for nodes).

# Editing Schematics

Now that you know how to draw a schematic using the various tools and components available to MICRO-CAP IV, we are ready to see how to modify the diagram. This is done by using the **Edit** pull-down menu accessed from the **Schematic Editor** window.

When you pull down the **Edit** menu, you are presented with six choices.

    1:Undo
    2:Cut
    3:Copy
    4:Paste
    5:Clear
    6:Select all

**1:Undo**   Undoes the effects of the last command.

**2:Cut**   Before using this or the next set of commands, you must select a component or group of components. You do this by choosing *Select* from the **Tools** menu (with the mouse or by typing **S**). You then either click on an element or click and drag to define a rectangle. Once you have selected a component or components, the Cut operation removes the selected elements but saves them in a clipboard. This and the following two operations are parallel to those used in windows-based word processors.

**3:Copy**   Copies the selected portion of the schematic to the clipboard, but unlike *Cut*, *Copy* does so without removing the selected items from the diagram.

**4:Paste**   Once you have saved components in the clipboard, you use the *Paste* command to insert them in the diagram at the cursor location. The clipboard continues to hold this information until you exit the program or replace the information with a Cut or Copy command. Therefore, you can paste material in more than one location on the diagram.

**5:Clear**   Removes the selected elements from the diagram, but does not affect the clipboard. If you draw an element or elements by mistake, simply select those elements and then use *Clear*.

**6:Select all**   Selects the entire circuit for copying or pasting.

The **Edit** pull-down menu allows you to move, remove, or copy portions of a circuit. If you simply want to change a component value or label, you need only select that component and then click a second time to display the label. You then edit the label directly from the keyboard.

## View Menu

The **View** pull-down menu in the **Schematic Editor** window contains nine selections.

1:Scale
2:Show comp text
3:Show grid text
4:Show node numbers
5:Show node voltages
6:Show pin connections
7:Show Region box
8:Search
9:Repeat search

**1:Scale**  Allows you to select the scale for drawing or viewing the circuit. If you have a large circuit and want to view it on a single screen, you can change the scale. Of course, higher scales make the components smaller and therefore harder to read. When you select this entry, you are presented with a second menu containing four scales: 1:1; 2:1; 4:1 and 8:1. You normally use 1:1.

If your diagram stretches beyond one page of a 1:1 screen, you can view it either by using a higher scale or by panning (scrolling) the schematic. Panning is performed by using the right mouse button. You click and hold down the button while dragging the mouse. The effect is similar to sliding a piece of paper across a desktop. From the keyboard you can press Ctrl+ an arrow key to move the view in the direction of the arrow. PgUp, PgDn, Home, and End move the view up, down, left, and right one page, respectively.

**2:Show comp text**  Toggles the item. That is, if it is already on, selecting it turns it off and vice versa. When it is on, a check mark appears to the left of the menu entry. The component text is used to identify the parameter or type of the component. You normally want this text to appear so you can identify components. You may want to temporarily disable the display if the circuit is extremely complex and components are densely packed.

**3:Show grid text**  Similar to the component text item discussed previously, except it refers to text you have added using the *Text* selection in the **Tools** menu.

**4:Show node numbers**  When you toggle this on, the assigned node numbers are displayed (in small boxes) directly on the schematic. It is important that you know assigned numbers if you choose to run a simulation and identify output parameters by node numbers. For example, you may want to display v(1) as the voltage on node 1. If you label the nodes with names, the numbers are not as important.

**5:Show node voltages**   Displays the last time-domain node voltages obtained in an analysis. This proves useful in displaying the steady-state dc bias voltages in an electronic circuit. We explore this in Tutorial #2.

**6:Show pin connections**   The **Shape Editor** adds pins to shapes to identify where the electrical connections of a component are located. Toggling this option on displays these pin locations.

**7:Show Region box**   Region boxes are used to define a region of the schematic that is to be stepped (repeated), printed, or plotted. The region box is adjusted by dragging the box corners with the left mouse button.

**8:Search**   MICRO-CAP IV offers four types of searches: component, parameter, text, and node number. If you select *Search*, you are presented with a **Search** window, allowing you to select one of the following four modes and then identify the search text.

- A *Component* search finds a circuit component whose name contains the given text.
- A *Parameter* search looks for components with the given parameter.
- A **Text** search looks for specified text that has been added using the *Text* selection in the **Tools** menu.
- A *Node number* search searches the circuit for a specified node number.

**9:Repeat search**   If you perform a search and find the first occurrence of the particular item, the ***Repeat search*** command repeats the search to locate any other entry that meets the specification.

## File Menu

The **File Menu** that is part of the **Schematic Editor** window contains six entries.

1:Unload circuit
2:Save circuit

3:Save circuit as
4:Print circuit
5:Plot schematic
6:Print netlist

**1:Unload circuit**  Unloads the currently active circuit from memory. If the file has changed since it was loaded, the system prompts you to save the circuit. You can disable this warning prompt from the **Preferences** window, which is part of the **Options** pull-down menu we discussed at the beginning of the tutorial.

**2:Save circuit**  Saves the circuit under the current file name without prompting the user to confirm the command.

**3:Save circuit as**  Displays a dialog box in which you enter the name under which you want the circuit saved. If you omit a data path, the current path is used.

**4:Print circuit**  Prints either a SPICE text circuit or a schematic. You should make sure you have selected the proper printer setup from the **Options** menu before you run a print command. You need only set up for your printer once. The selections are stored in the program when you exit. This print command is different from the print commands contained in the **Print** pull-down menu that is part of the **System** window. The print command prints only the circuit, while the other commands print an entire window.

**5:Plot schematic**  Similar to the previous command but for a plotter rather than printer.

**6:Print netlist**  A netlist includes the components used, the nodes to which the components are connected, the parameters of the components, a listing of relevant command statements (such as .MODEL statements), and a component tally. If a node has a label assigned to it, the label is used instead of the node number. Ground is always node zero.

When you select *Print netlist*, a submenu allows you to expand macros and subcircuits or .DEFINE statements. If you choose to expand .DEFINE statements, component labels are replaced with the actual component values.

Figure 47 shows the PRLC circuit we used in this tutorial along with the netlist for this circuit.

## SPICE Files

MICRO-CAP IV can handle SPICE text file circuit descriptions. These may be created externally with a word processor or a text editor, or internally using the program's text editor.

To create a SPICE file, pull down the **File** menu and select *2:New SPICE file*. This opens a text file and positions the text cursor at the upper-left-hand corner of the screen. Note that since you are now in text mode, you can no longer access menus by simply typing the menu letter. If you want to access menus from the keyboard, press the Alt key in combination with the appropriate letter key.

You type the SPICE statements for the circuit and then store the circuit by pulling down the **File** menu (or typing Alt+F) and selecting *3:Save Circuit as*. Then give the circuit a name. SPICE circuit file names do not require or assume an extension. There is no default extension (such as .CIR). You can either choose an extension or save the file without one.

MICRO-CAP IV can convert schematics to SPICE text file format. That is, you can draw and store a schematic using the MICRO-CAP Schematic Editor. Then the final circuit can be converted to a SPICE listing. This converted program description can then be run through a generic or PSpice-compatible program. You may wish to do this to compare results. The conversion is performed by the TOSPICE.EXE program, which is included on your disk. The program is executed from the DOS prompt with a single command line as follows:

**TOSPICE[DRIVE:][PATH]INFILE[.CIR]**
**[DRIVE:][PATH][OUTFILE[.EXT]]**
 **/ANALYSIS /SPICETYPE** ↵

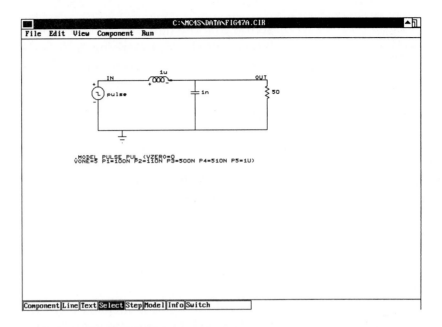

Figure 47

**INFILE** is the name of the MICRO-CAP IV schematic file to be converted. The extension .CIR is optional. You may prefix a drive and path if necessary. **OUTFILE** is the name of the SPICE text file to be created. The extension is optional. You may prefix a drive and path if desired. For both INFILE and OUTFILE, if no drive or path is specified, the program uses the drive and path for the current data director. **ANALYSIS** can be any combination of the following:

**T** Transient Analysis
**A** ac analysis
**D** dc analysis

**SPICETYPE** can be either

1 Generic: SPICE 2G.6
2 PSpice

Since generic SPICE does not have all of the models that MICRO-CAP IV contains, some features (for example, Laplace and function sources) cannot be translated. In such cases you should choose **PSpice**.

As an example, suppose you type the following command:

**TOSPICE C:\DATA\RCA3040.CIR B:\3040 /TAD /1** ⏎

This loads the MICRO-CAP IV file RCA3040.CIR from the C:\DATA subdirectory and creates a generic SPICE text file called 3040. This SPICE file contains appropriate statements to perform transient, ac, and dc analyses. The converted file is saved in the root directory of the disk in drive B.

## Examples

1. Draw the circuit shown in Figure 48.

**Solution:** You could go through the trouble of drawing it component by component, but we choose to use the **Copy** command to cut the work in half. We begin by drawing the first op-amp circuit, as shown in Figure 49. Then we select the entire circuit (by choosing either **Select all** from the **Edit** menu or **Select** from the **Tools** menu and then clicking and dragging a box around the first op-amp). We select **Copy**

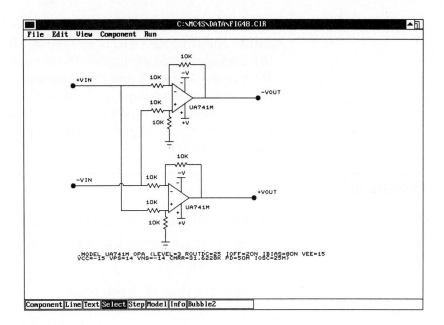

Figure 48

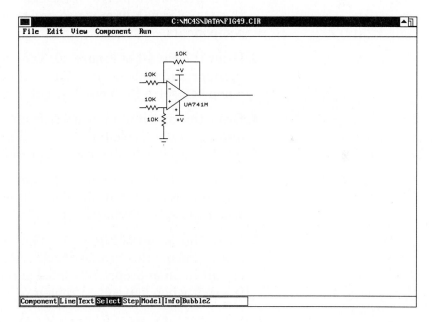

Figure 49

from the **Edit** pull-down menu. This copies the selected circuit to the clipboard without erasing it from the screen (as the *Cut* command would do). We then select *Paste* from the **Edit** menu and click and drag the second circuit to the correct position. We complete the circuit with the supply and other components. Finally we select *Model* from the **Tools** menu to copy the .MODEL statements for the 741 op-amp from the library.

## Problems

1. You have the following sample circuits on your disk:

   TL1, U741, CURVES, PRLC, DIFFAMP, GUMMEL, L1, F4, TRIODE

   Retrieve each of these, print each circuit on your printer, and then redraw each one yourself.

2. You want to create the AM waveform $\sin(2\pi \times 1000t)\sin(2\pi \times 10^5 t)$. Design a circuit that produces this waveform. You may use any type of sources and components.

3. Draw the circuit of Figure 50. Then store the circuit in an appropriately labeled file. You will need to retrieve it when you solve Problem 2 in Tutorial 2.

4. Draw the circuit of Figure 51. Then store the circuit in an appropriately labeled file. You will need to retrieve it when you solve Problem 3 in Tutorial 2.

5. Draw the circuit of Figure 52. Then store the circuit in an appropriately labeled file. You will need to retrieve it when you solve Problem 4 in Tutorial 2.

6. Draw the circuit of Figure 53. The controlled voltage source means this is a feedback system. Then store the circuit in an appropriately labeled file. You will need to retrieve it when you solve Problem 2 in Tutorial 3.

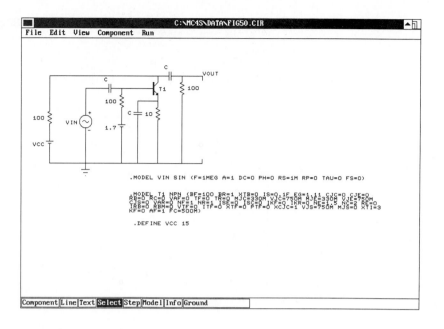

Figure 50

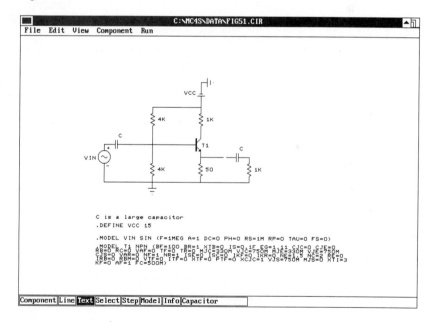

Figure 51

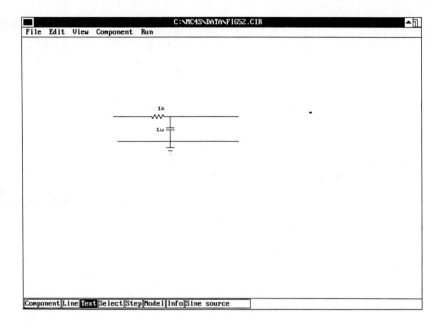

Figure 52

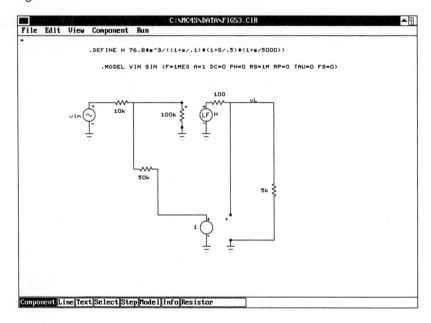

Figure 53

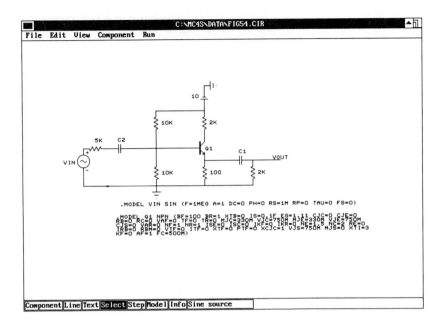

Figure 54

7. Draw the circuit of Figure 54. Then store the circuit in an appropriately labeled file. You will need to retrieve it when you solve Problem 3 in Tutorial 3.

8. Draw the circuit of Figure 55. Then store the circuit in an appropriately labeled file. You will need to retrieve it when you solve Problem 4 in Tutorial 3.

9. Draw the circuit of Figure 56. Then store the circuit in an appropriately labeled file. You will need to retrieve it when you solve Problem 5 in Tutorial 3.

10. Draw the circuit of Figure 57. Then store the circuit in an appropriately labeled file. You will need to retrieve it when you solve Problem 7 in Tutorial 3.

11. Draw the circuit of Figure 58. Then store the circuit in an appropriately labeled file. You will need to retrieve it when you solve Problem 9 in Tutorial 3.

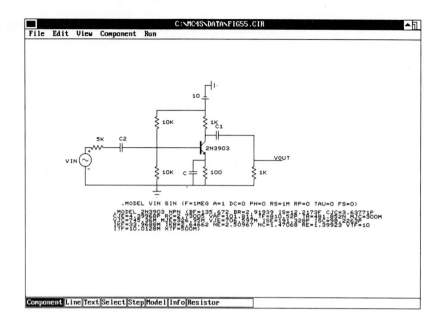

Figure 55

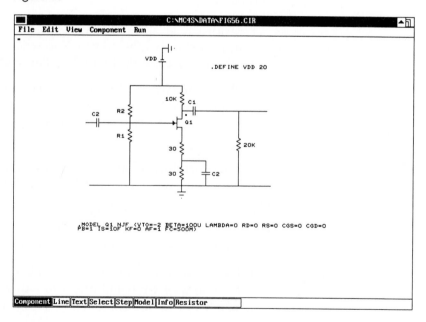

Figure 56

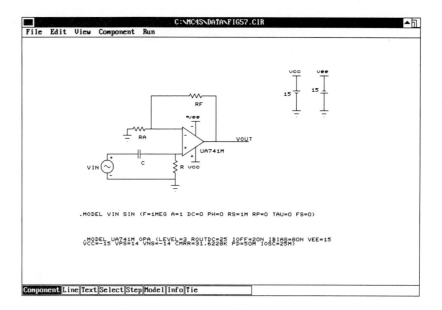

Figure 57

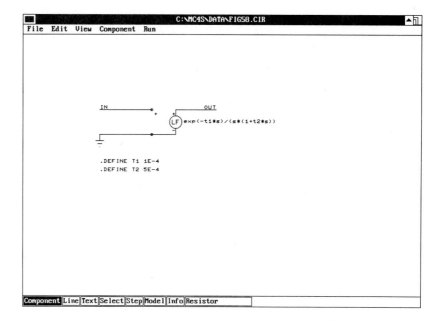

Figure 58

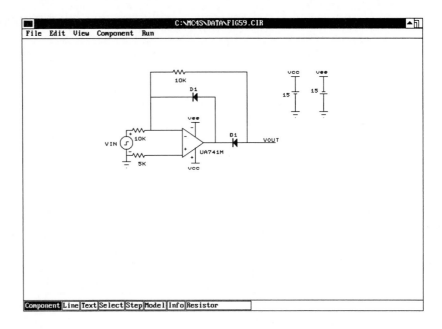

Figure 59

12. Draw the circuit of Figure 59. Then store the circuit in an appropriately labeled file. You will need to retrieve it when you solve Problem 3 in Tutorial 4.

13. Draw the circuit of Figure 60. Then store the circuit in an appropriately labeled file. You will need to retrieve it when you solve Problem 4 in Tutorial 4.

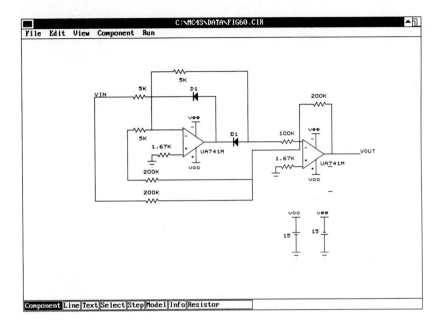

Figure 60

# 2

---

# Transient Analysis

---

## Introduction

If you have gone through Tutorial #1, you can now draw any circuit on the monitor. Tutorials #2, #3, and #4 explore the various forms of analysis you can perform using MICRO-CAP IV.

Transient analysis is used to plot time waveforms at various points in the circuit. It involves generating a new set of equations dynamically for each time point, solving these equations, printing and graphing the solutions, and setting up a new set of equations whose contents depend on the prior solutions. Transient analysis evolves from the state space approach, which you may have been exposed to in your systems courses.

You begin by drawing a circuit, either by entering each component, as described in Tutorial #1, or by retrieving a network from the data file. We illustrate transient analysis using the differential amplifier circuit, which is one of the files already stored in the program. If you currently have any circuit in the **Schematic Editor** window, unload it using

the **File** pull-down menu. Then recall the differential amplifier file from memory by using the **File** pull-down menu
from the main (top) menu bar, selecting *3:Load schematic,*
and then loading DIFFAMP.CIR (you can scroll down to
DIFFAMP using the mouse or the arrow keys, or type **D** to
jump down to the first entry starting with the letter "D").
Your screen should look like Figure 61.

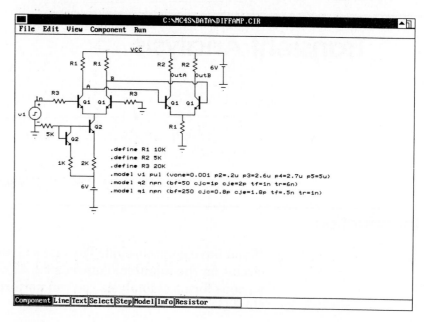

Figure 61

Once you have the network on the screen, initiate the analysis by pulling down the **Run** menu and selecting *1:Tran-
sient analysis.* Alternatively, you can use the keyboard in
one of two ways. Either type the menu identifier followed by
the entry

**R; 1**

or use the hotkey (identified on the pull-down menu) by simply pressing Alt+**1.**

After you initiate the transient analysis, you are presented with the **Transient Analysis Limits** window. We begin this tutorial with a discussion of this window. We then discuss each of the menu selections available in the **Transient Analysis.**

## Transient Analysis Limits

After activating the transient analysis, you are presented with a window showing limits used in the analysis. When you store a circuit, the selected limits are stored with it. If you create a new circuit, default limits are used until you choose different values. The limits stored in the differential amplifier circuit are shown in Figure 62. If you want to change any of the analysis limits, you just click the mouse on that limit and type in the new value.

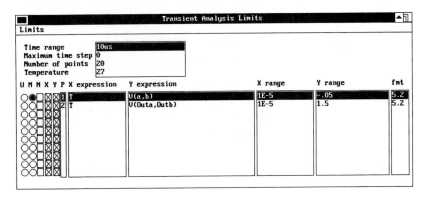

Figure 62

We now describe each of the analysis limits. However, if you are impatient to see an analysis run, you can simply pull down the **Transient** menu (press Alt+**T**, or access this menu with the mouse) and select **_Run_** (or press the F2 function key).

## Numeric Limits Fields

The upper portion of the window contains a field with four entries.

### Time Range

This is used to specify the time over which the simulation is performed. You can specify two parameters: the starting time (tmin) and the ending time (tmax). The format for simulation time is

**tmax[,tmin]**

When you specify input parameters, the terms in square brackets are optional. If they are omitted, the default values are used. The default value for tmin is zero. You are not permitted to specify negative values for either of these times. The example of Figure 62 shows a time range of 10us. This means the simulation time runs from 0 to 10 microseconds. We could have specified the same range by entering **10us,0**.

### Maximum Time Step

MICRO-CAP IV simulates operation of a circuit by stepping in time. Each time the program calculates parameters, these are compared with the previous calculation. If a circuit contains capacitance or inductance, the program monitors the time rate of change of the charge and flux. Internal algorithms control the size of this derivative. If it is too large, the time step is decreased. If it is too small, the time step is increased up to the specified maximum. The internal algorithm controls accuracy of the results. If the maximum time increment is too large, the resolution suffers, while if it is too small, the program takes a long time to run. You can often smooth a resulting curve by reducing the maximum time step.

The default value for the time step is (tmax–tmin)/50. This means that 50 iterations are performed over the length of the simulation. The program uses the default value either if you leave the field blank on the **Transient Analysis Limits** window or if you enter zero for the maximum time step, as we have done in this example. (Clearly, if the program ran with a zero time step, you would have to wait forever for a single plot to develop.)

### Number of Points

This specification is used for numeric output (that is, a table, as opposed to a graph). It sets the number of points to be printed (number of rows in the printout table). The default value is 51, which corresponds to the default value for the time step. If the specified points do not fall directly on values used in the iteration, the printed value is interpolated from calculated values.

### Temperature

Temperature enters into the parameter equations for devices and components. One or more temperature values (in degrees Celsius) can be specified for the analysis. The format is

**High [,Low[,Step]]**

The square brackets indicate you can omit Step, or you can omit both Low and Step. The default value for Low is High while the default value for Step is the difference between High and Low. Therefore, if only one value is specified, the simulation runs at that temperature. If two values are specified, the simulation runs at those two values, the Low and High temperatures. For example, an entry of **27,25** runs the simulation twice at 25 and 27 degrees Celsius (27 degrees is room temperature). An entry of **35,20,5** runs the simulation at 20, 25, 30, and 35 degrees.

## Waveform Options Fields

We now turn our attention to the wide table occupying the lower half of the **Transient Analysis Limits** window of Figure 62. The table contains 11 columns, 6 of which are used to select waveform options. Each of these is described below.

### U

The U (User) column contains circles called radio buttons. They are enabled by clicking the mouse on that entry, and once enabled they are filled in and dark. When the U button is enabled, the Y expression waveform in this row is saved to a user file. We discussed this in Tutorial #1 when we addressed sources. One of the sources we discussed is specified by a file, and these files can be generated during a transient analysis.

## M

The M (Monte Carlo) radio button is enabled if you want to perform a Monte Carlo analysis. Only one waveform can be selected for Monte Carlo analysis (that is, there can be only one dark button in the entire M column). We discuss Monte Carlo analysis later in this tutorial. For now you should be aware that enabling the radio button is not the only thing you need to do to execute a Monte Carlo analysis.

## N

The N (Numeric) column is in the form of a toggle box. It is used to select waveforms for numeric output. Numeric output is directed to a parallel or serial port, the screen, or a file, depending on the selection made in the **Printer setup for text** window.

## X

This toggle box determines whether the X variable is linear or logarithmic. An X in the box indicates linear, while the absence of an X indicates the scale is a log scale.

## Y

This is the same as the X toggle box, **X**, except it determines whether the Y variable is linear or logarithmic.

## P

When several variables are plotted, you have a choice of superimposing them on the same set of axes or having them appear on separate, nonoverlapping graphs. The numeric entry in the P column is a number from 1 to 9. This indicates to which group the particular waveform is assigned. If you use the same number for several rows, these waveforms are plotted on the same set of axes. If the ranges are not the same, the plot uses the union of the individual ranges. MICRO-CAP IV analyzes equations independent of units. For example, a plot with a range from 0 to 1 could be used for a voltage curve ranging from 0 to 1 volts and simultaneously for a current curve ranging from 0 to 1 amps.

The example of Figure 62 creates two curves plotted on two separate sets of axes. If you want the two curves superimposed, you assign the same P number to both.

**Expression Fields**

The remaining five columns relate to the expressions to be plotted.

### X Expression

This field specifies the expressions for the X-axis variable. In most cases this is a time variable, but it could be another parameter. For example, you can plot a hysteresis curve, in which case the X expressions may be an input voltage.

### Y Expression

This field specifies the expressions for the Y-axis variables. These may be simple voltages or currents, or they could be more complex math expressions, such as power. For example, you might have an electronic circuit where you plot V(VCC)*I(VCC). If VCC is the label assigned to the dc source, this plot represents the power flow from the source. Alternatively, you can plot the output/input voltage ratio in decibels by specifying DB(VOUT/VIN), where you have labeled the input voltage as VIN and the output as VOUT.

The "Function Sources" section in Tutorial #1 summarizes the various functions and equations available in MICRO-CAP IV. We do not repeat that list here, but we do take a moment to list the variety of variables you can specify.

**V(A)**    The voltage at node A. If the node is not labeled, you can use its number.

**V(A,B)**   Voltage at node A minus voltage at node B.

**V(D)**    Voltage across the device called D.

**I(D)**    Current through the device called D.

| | |
|---|---|
| **T** | Time. |
| **F** | Frequency (in Hz). |
| **S** | Complex frequency = $2*\pi*F*j$. |
| **V(A)\*I(A)** | Power. |

Note that in the example of Figure 62, we plot two expressions, V(a,b) and V(Outa,Outb). These represent differential voltages between pairs of nodes. The nodes are labeled on the schematic of Figure 61.

MICRO-CAP IV can perform a variety of signal processing functions. In specifying the Y expression for plotting, you can choose any of the 12 different processing functions listed below:

| | |
|---|---|
| **FFT(x)** | Forward Fourier transform of waveform x |
| **IFT(X)** | Inverse Fourier transform of spectrum X |
| **CONJ(X)** | Conjugate of spectrum X |
| **CS(x,y)** | Cross spectrum of X and Y = CONJ(FFT(x)\*FFT(y)) |
| **AS(x)** | Auto spectrum of spectrum X = CS(x,x) |
| **CC(x,y)** | Cross-correlation of waveforms x and y = IFT(CS(x,y)) |
| **AC(x)** | Auto-correlation of waveform x = IFT(AS(x)) |
| **COH(x,y)** | Coherence of waveforms x and y = CC(x,y)/sqr(AC(x(0)\*AC(y(0))) |
| **REAL(X)** | Real part of spectrum X produced by FFT |
| **IMAG(X)** | Imaginary part of spectrum X produced by FFT |
| **MAG(X)** | Magnitude of spectrum X produced by FFT |
| **PHASE(X)** | Phase of spectrum X produced by FFT |

You can gain familiarity with some of these functions by experimenting with the circuits stored in your program. In particular, FFT1.CIR demonstrates the use of some functions in transient analysis. You should experiment with that circuit and plot the various FFT parameters as you vary the length of the time interval. See if this agrees with what you learned about FFT in your digital signal processing course.

### X range

This sets the scale ranges for the X waveforms. The format is

### High[,Low].

In our example we have a single entry, 1E–5. This means that X runs from 0 to 10 microseconds. Note that this matches the time range of the simulation. To have MICRO-CAP IV automatically set the range, place the cursor on the appropriate field and type **auto**. We give a faster way to enter **auto** in the next section in our discussion of the **Limits** menu. The range must be a subset of the simulation time. That is, you cannot plot a response for a range of values if the simulation was not performed for that range. If you use the auto entry, the program must run the entire simulation prior to setting the plotting range. You do not see the result plotted in real time.

### Y range

This is the same as X range, except it is for the Y variable. You can enter **auto** in this field for MICRO-CAP IV to scale the range automatically so the plots fill the graph.

### fmt

The fmt (format) field controls the format of printed numbers used in the tabular printout or the cursor mode (we discuss this later). The number to the left of the decimal point sets the space for digits to the left of the decimal point in the printed numbers. Similarly, the number to the right of the decimal point sets the number of digits to the right of the decimal point. The example shows 5.2, which means printouts contain up to five digits to the left of the decimal point and two to the right (that is, hundredths).

**Limits Pull-Down Menu**

In the upper-left-hand corner of the **Transient Analysis Limits** window is the **Limits** pull-down menu. This menu can save you a lot of time. It contains two entries: ***Default all***, and ***Default blank***. If you select ***1:Default all***, the program inserts "auto" into all range fields with valid plot numbers. If you select ***2:Default blank***, the program inserts "auto" into all blank range fields with valid plot numbers.

## Running the Analysis

Once you are satisfied with the analysis limits, you are ready to run the analysis. Run the analysis by pulling down the **Transient** menu and clicking ***1:Run***. (Since the **Transient** pull-down menu is not highlighted, you cannot access it by pressing **T**. Instead, you must press Alt+**T** to pull down the menu from the keyboard.) Instead of doing all of this work, you can simply press the F2 function key. The transient analysis is produced, as shown in Figure 63.

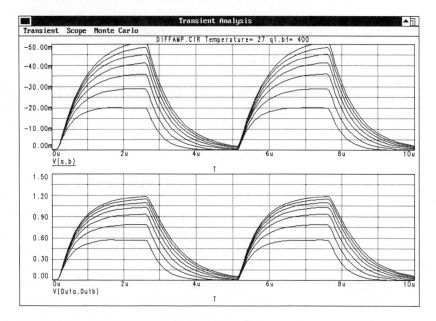

Figure 63

You can stop the simulation at any time by pressing the Esc key. While the simulation is running, you can press **P** to toggle numeric displays. When the display is on, the X and Y values for each waveform are printed on the screen as the calculations are performed.

Note that we have plotted two waveforms on the two graphs of Figure 63. If you watched the program produce the output, you saw that the simulation ran seven separate times generating a family of seven curves for each variable. This happened because we selected a stepping option in the parameters stored on your disk. We discuss stepping in detail later in this tutorial. If you ran the simple example in Part I of this manual, you are already experienced at using this option.

Below the title bar for the **Transient Analysis** window (Figure 63) are three pull-down menus: **Transient**, **Scope**, and **Monte Carlo**. We now discuss each of these.

## Transient Menu

Once you select *Transient Analysis* from the **Run** menu, you can pull down the **Transient** menu either with the mouse or by pressing Alt+**T**. The menu contains seven selections:

> 1:Run
> 2:Limits
> 3:Options
> 4:Stepping
> 5:Numeric output
> 6:Plot analysis
> 7:State Variables Editor

**1:Run**

You select this menu entry to run the simulation.

**2:Limits**

Note that this item is checked. It opens the **Transient Analysis Limits** window so you can change limits. The **Transient Analysis Limits** window is automatically opened when you select *1:Transient analysis* from the **Run** menu, so you access this from the **Transient** menu only to make changes following a simulation run.

## 3:Options

Clicking on *3:Options* presents the **Transient options** window, as shown in Figure 64. This window is divided into four areas: Run options, State variables, Analysis options, and Other options. Selections are made by clicking the mouse on the appropriate button or box. You can leave the **Options** window either by initiating the run (pull down the **Transient** menu and select *Run,* or press the F2 function key), by erasing the window (click on the box to the left of the title), or by pressing the Esc key.

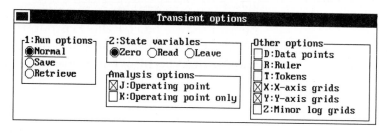

Figure 64

### Run Options

You have three choices. *Normal* produces a normal run. *Save* saves the entire simulation for later retrieval. *Retrieve* retrieves a saved simulation for review.

### State Variables

*Zero* sets the initial capacitor voltages and inductor currents to zero prior to each temperature or step run. *Read* reads the initial voltages and currents from a previously saved disk file prior to each temperature or stepping run. *Leave* does not change the initial voltages and currents prior to each run. They remain unchanged from either the prior run, the last file read, or the last edit.

## Analysis Options

*Operating point* forces the simulator to calculate the dc operating point (due to the t=0 values of the sources) prior to each run. It is needed for most nonlinear circuits. *Operating point only* forces the simulator to calculate the dc operating point and then terminate the run. This can be used to find quiescent values in a circuit. To do so, complete the run and then press the F3 function key to end the simulation. Then pull down the **View** menu and select *5:Show node voltages*. The result is shown in Figure 65, which is still the differential amplifier example. Before displaying this figure, we used the **View** menu to remove both component text and grid text so as not to clutter the diagram. Before continuing, you should go back to the **Options** window and disable *Operating point only*. Otherwise, the next simulation you perform will stop after calculating the operating point.

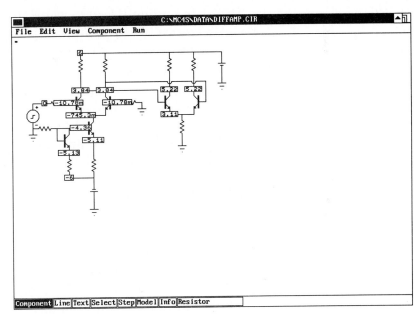

Figure 65

### Other Options

**Data points** Causes the actual data points of the simulation to be marked on the plot.

**Ruler:** Selects ruler marks in lieu of full screen graph divider lines.

**Tokens** A token is a distinctive mark on a graph. For example, in multiple graphs on the same set of axes, one curve can be marked with open circles while another is marked with squares. An X in this box adds tokens to all but the first waveform of each group. A token also appears next to each axis scale identifier to help in the identification process.

**X-axis grids** Draws vertical grids or rule marks.

**Y-axis grids** Draws horizontal grids or rule marks.

**Minor log grids** Used to switch the minor log grids (between powers of 10) on and off. It applies only to logarithmic scales.

## 4:Stepping

Component parameters may be stepped from one value to another, producing multiple runs with multiple output waveforms. You activate this feature by selecting **4:Stepping** from the **Transient** menu and then entering instructions in the dialog box. The dialog box for the differential amplifier example is shown in Figure 66.

In producing some of the figures in this part of the manual, we have printed only the front window. You can always erase the front (active) window by clicking on the box to the left of the window title or by pressing the Esc key. You probably will not be erasing windows as you go along, so the other active windows will show on your screen. Figure 66 shows this for the **Stepping** window. You have to struggle a bit to pick out the **Stepping** window in the middle of the screen. It has a title bar, four text entries, and two radio buttons. We now describe each of these entries.

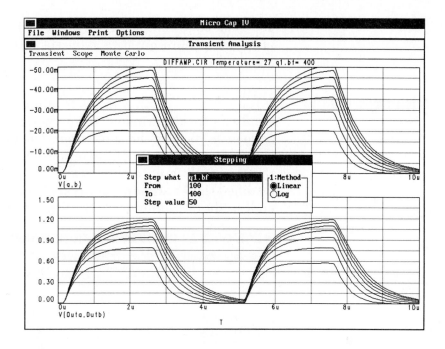

Figure 66

## Step what

In this entry you specify which parameter you want to change. To step the value of a component, you enter the name of that component. For example, if you named one or more resistors R1, you would enter **R1** to step their values. In the case of stepping device parameters, you enter the device name, a period, and the parameter you want to vary. In the differential amplifier example, we are stepping the forward beta of the transistor labeled Q1, so we enter **Q1.BF**. (Case makes no difference to MICRO-CAP IV, so don't be concerned if your screen shows q1.bf instead of Q1.BF.)

## Limits

*From* specifies the starting value of the parameter. *To* specifies the ending value of the parameter. *Step value* specifies the amount by which to step the parameter. In our example circuit we are varying the beta of transistor Q1 from 100 to

400 in steps of 50. That is why we obtained seven separate plots. They represent beta values of 100, 150, 200, 250, 300, 350, and 400.

**5:Numeric Output**

If you have placed an X in the **N** column of the **Transient Analysis Limits** window, the numeric output is displayed as soon as you run the simulation. The display is in a window in front of the graphical output plots. Figure 67 shows this for the differential amplifier example, where we have modified the **Transient Analysis Limits** window by adding an X in the **N** column for both of the plotted variables.

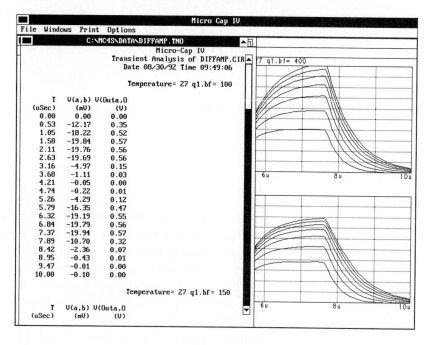

Figure 67

You can scroll through the numeric values using the arrows, the page up or page down key, or by typing Esc+**End** to reach the end of the list. You can remove the numeric window by pressing the Esc key. Once the window is removed,

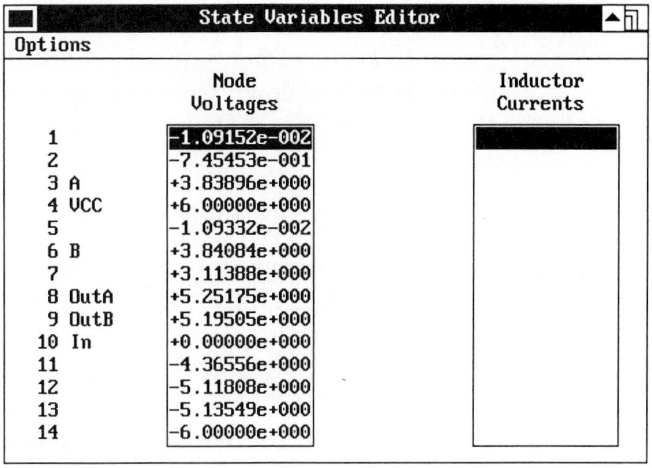

```
┌────────────────────────────────────────────────────────┐
│ ■         State Variables Editor              ▲ ⌐│
│ Options                                                 │
│ ┌──────────────────────────────────────────────────────┐│
│              Node                      Inductor         │
│              Voltages                  Currents         │
│      1       ┌──────────────┐          ┌──────────────┐ │
│      2       │-1.09152e-002 │          │██████████████│ │
│      3 A     │-7.45453e-001 │          │              │ │
│      4 VCC   │+3.83896e+000 │          │              │ │
│      5       │+6.00000e+000 │          │              │ │
│      6 B     │-1.09332e-002 │          │              │ │
│      7       │+3.84084e+000 │          │              │ │
│      8 OutA  │+3.11388e+000 │          │              │ │
│      9 OutB  │+5.25175e+000 │          │              │ │
│     10 In    │+5.19505e+000 │          │              │ │
│     11       │+0.00000e+000 │          │              │ │
│     12       │-4.36556e+000 │          │              │ │
│     13       │-5.11808e+000 │          │              │ │
│     14       │-5.13549e+000 │          │              │ │
│              │-6.00000e+000 │          └──────────────┘ │
│              └──────────────┘                           │
└────────────────────────────────────────────────────────┘
```

Figure 68

you can activate it again by selecting *5:Numeric output* from the **Transient** menu.

**6:Plot Analysis**

This command generates output to a plotter or file according to the instructions in the Plotter setup dialog box. The plotter is not your printer. This command is used only if you have a separate plotter connected to your computer. The option is selected after the analysis is complete. The same waveforms plotted on the screen are then sent to the plotter or to the file.

**7:State Variables Editor**

This command activates the State Variables Editor. After you run the simulation, you use the editor to view and edit node voltages and inductor currents. The **State Variables Editor** for the differential amplifier example is shown in Figure 68, which shows fourteen node voltages. When a node has been assigned a label, that name appears to the right of the node number. Our differential amplifier circuit does not contain any inductors, so the right portion of this editor window is blank.

You normally do not change these values unless you want to explore the effects of an initial condition variation. You can edit individual entries, or you can use the local **Options** menu to perform more general editing. The local **Options** menu is pulled down from the upper-left-hand corner of the **State Variables Editor** window. This menu contains four entries.

*1:Clear*   Immediately sets every state variable to zero.

*2:Read*   Immediately reads the state variables from the disk file CIRCUITNAME.TOP. For example, if you were running the differential amplifier example, you would have to have state variables already stored in a file with the name DIFFAMP.TOP. Such a file would exist if you had executed the *Write* option, as described below.

*3:Write*   Writes the state variables to the disk file CIRCUITNAME.TOP.

*4:Print*   Prints the initial conditions in text format.

This completes our discussion of the seven entries on the **Transient** pull-down menu. We now turn our attention to the other two menus available in transient analysis. Press the Esc key to clear any windows that are active until you return to the simulation output plot.

## Scope Menu

The **Scope** menu is used to select various scope commands. The menu provides you with 11 choices.

1:Scale mode
2:Cursor mode
3:Text absolute mode
4:Text relative mode
5:Zoom-In
6:Zoom-Out
7:Remove all text
8:Autoscale
9:Restore limit scales
A:Fast scroll
B:Numeric format

## 1:Scale mode

In this mode waveforms can be contracted, expanded, and scrolled (or panned).

## 2:Cursor mode

In this mode two moveable cursors are used to display numeric values of the waveform, as shown in Figure 69.

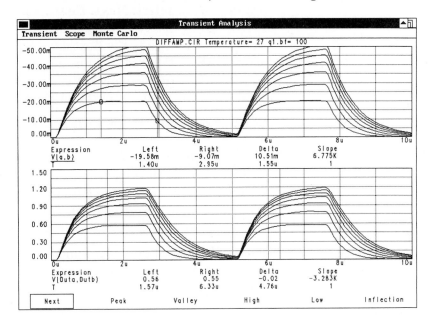

Figure 69

The left-hand cursor is positioned by clicking and dragging the left mouse button. We have placed the left-hand cursor between 1 and 2 microseconds, and the corresponding point on the lowest curve is marked. The right-hand cursor, which is positioned using the right mouse button, has been placed a little to the left of 3 microseconds. Below the graph are two text lines listing parameters of the two cursor values.

The first line presents the values of V(a,b). Note that they are −19.58 mv and −9.07 mv, respectively. The line also indicates the difference between these two points (10.51 mv) and the slope of a line joining the two points.

If you look at the bottom of the window, you note six modes from which to select: **Next, Peak, Valley, High, Low,** and **Inflection**. Currently a box is around **Next**, which indicates that you can move to the next data point using the keyboard arrows. The left cursor is moved from the keyboard by pressing the left or right arrow keys. To move the right cursor, you press the Shift and one of the arrow keys.

You can select the **Peak** (local maximum) mode by clicking with the mouse or by typing **P**. You now are in a position to automatically place the cursors at the peaks of the waveform. You position the left cursor by pressing the left or right arrow key. This moves the cursor to the first peak to the left or right of its starting location. The right cursor is moved by holding down the Shift key while pressing an arrow key.

The **Valley** (local minimum) mode is similar to the **Peak** mode, but it locates valleys of the curve.

The **High** mode is used to select the global maximum of the curve, that is, the maximum peak. Select this mode and then use either arrow key to move the left cursor and Shift plus either arrow key to move the right cursor.

The **Low** mode is similar to the **High** mode, except it locates the global minimum.

The **Inflection** mode locates points where the second derivative of the waveform goes through zero (that is, changes sign). The arrow keys locate such points for the left cursor (starting at its current location) and Shift plus the arrow keys move the right cursor.

**Note**: We hope you are trying these operations for the differential amplifier example. If you are doing so and are thinking about what you are seeing on the screen, you are probably thinking that the **High** and **Low** modes are yielding the opposite of what you expect. However, keep in mind that V(a,b) is negative, so the high values are at the bottom of the graph and the low values are at the top. Additionally, since the output curve for this example asymptotically approaches the steady state values, it is not a good example to illustrate the use of **Peak** and **Valley**. You may get some incorrect answers due to round-off error in the process of comparing adjacent slopes.

| | |
|---|---|
| **3:Text absolute mode** | In this mode, new text added to the plot maintains its absolute position in the window, regardless of how the graph is panned. |
| **4:Text relative mode** | In this mode, new text added to the plot maintains its position relative to the waveforms, regardless of how the plot is panned. |
| **5:Zoom-In** | This command expands the graph. |
| **6:Zoom-Out** | This is the opposite of *Zoom In*. |
| **7:Remove all text** | This removes all text added while in the text absolute or text relative modes. |
| **8:Autoscale** | This automatically scales the waveform to fill the assigned area of the screen. In the differential amplifier example simulation result, note that the final stepped waveform for V(a,b) extends slightly above the top of the graph. If you enable *Autoscale*, the scales are adjusted so that the waveform no longer "saturates" the graph. |
| **9:Restore limit scales** | This restores the scales of every waveform to those entered in the **Analysis Limits** window. |
| **A:Fast scroll** | You scroll, or pan, the waveform using the right button of the mouse. When you press the right mouse button, a hand appears at the cursor location on the screen. Move the mouse |

while holding the button to scroll the waveform. As you pan a waveform with the mouse, the waveform is updated. If the *Fast scroll* option is disabled and you move the mouse a distance on the screen, you see the waveform update in steps from the original position to the final position. With *Fast scroll* activated the intermediate steps are eliminated and the repositioned output is developed more quickly.

**B:Numeric format**

This lets you change the numeric format of the cursor printouts. It works the same as the **fmt** entries on the analysis limits window.

# Probe

PROBE is a powerful tool that allows you to view waveforms at various points in the schematic, just as you would use a probe from a laboratory oscilloscope. PROBE performs the transient analysis, saves the entire analysis in a disk file, and then allows you to probe points in the circuit. PROBE functions like a normal simulation, but you need not specify in advance which outputs to plot.

Let's continue working with the differential amplifier schematic. Exit any run that you currently are in (press F3), and you should have the schematic on the screen. If you are just starting, load the differential amplifier schematic. Before running the simulation, pull down the **Run** menu and select *4:Probe mode*. This places you in the probe mode. Then pull down the **Run** menu again (note that *Probe mode* is checked) and select *Transient Analysis*. The program runs the simulation, which may take a while since your computer is doing more work than it does to plot one or two variables. After the run, your display should look like Figure 70.

The circuit (or part of it) is on the left, and a transient analysis window is on the right. The window has four pull-down menus, **Probe, Vertical, Horizontal,** and **Scope.** We now describe the entries in each of these menus.

The **Probe** pull-down menu contains 8 entries.

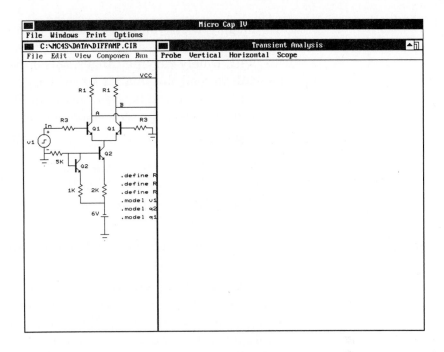

Figure 70

**1:New run** PROBE stores results in data files on the disk. These files are named CIRCUITNAME.TSA. If you have not changed the circuit since the last PROBE run, the program does not rerun the simulation when you go to probe mode. If you have changed the circuit, the program detects this and performs a new run. If you have not changed the circuit but still want to have a new simulation (for example, if you changed a component model), you select

*1:New run* from the **Probe** menu.

**2:Remove** Lets the user remove a single waveform from the plot by selecting it from a scrollable list.

**3:Remove all** Removes all waveforms from the plot.

**4:One trace** Selects the single trace mode. When a new waveform is selected, it replaces the previous one.

**5:Many traces** Used to select multiple traces for the PROBE waveform display. Up to six waveforms can be displayed. As you probe various points, the new waveforms are added to the diagram. If you have multiple waveforms with widely varying ranges, this option may make it difficult to read the smaller waveforms since the vertical axis will scale for the largest waveform. In such cases you may want to select the ***One trace*** option.

**6:Save all**   Causes all PROBE variables to be saved.

**7:Save V&I only**   Causes only voltages and currents to be saved during the save run. If these are the only variables you will want to probe, this option speeds things up and saves disk space.

**8:Options**   Accesses the **Options** window, as described earlier in this tutorial.

The **Vertical** and **Horizontal** pull-down menus contain identical entries. These are used to determine the variables, operators, and scale types (log or linear) used for the horizontal and vertical axes. When you select ***Save V&I only*** from the **Probe** menu, many of the selections are not available to you (that is, only the voltage or current can be selected for display). If you have saved all variables, you can choose to display

Voltage
Current
Resistance (displays the resistance when the mouse is
   clicked on a resistor)
Charge (displays charge when the mouse is clicked on a
   capacitor)
Capacitance (displays capacitance associated with the
   charge)
Flux (displays flux when the mouse is clicked on an
   inductor)
Inductance (displays inductance associated with the
   charge)
B field (displays B field when the mouse is clicked on a
   core)

H field (displays H field when the mouse is clicked on a core)

Time (usually selected for horizontal display)

Let's first examine a node voltage. Suppose you want to display the voltage at the node labeled A on the schematic. You would select *0:Voltage* on the **Vertical** menu and *9:Time* on the **Horizontal** menu. Position the cursor on node A and click the left button. The result is shown in Figure 71.

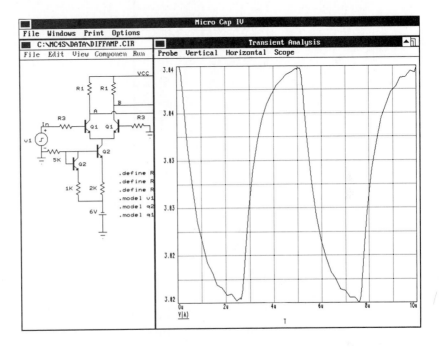

Figure 71

If you selected *5:Many traces* from the **Probe** menu, you can click additional nodes and superimpose up to six waveforms.

In addition to node voltages, you can also select lead-to-lead voltages. First remove all waveforms using the **Probe** pull-down menu and selecting *3:Remove all*, or by pressing the F9 function key. Then position the cursor midway between the base and collector of the left Q1, and click the left mouse button. You then plot either VCB or VBC, depending on whether the cursor is closer to the base or closer to the collector. The result is shown in Figure 72.

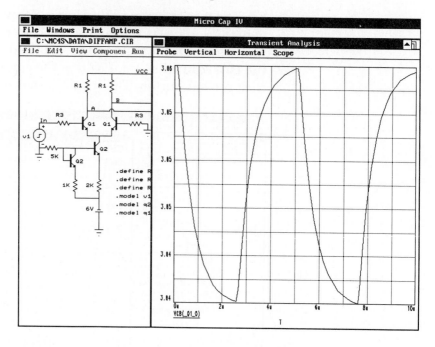

Figure 72

If a portion of the circuit extends beyond the visible region, you can scroll the circuit using the right mouse button.

PROBE is a very powerful tool in debugging circuits. If the output is not what you expect it to be, you can often determine the cause of the discrepancy by probing intermediate points in the circuit.

## Monte Carlo Analysis

In the real world circuits do not behave in the simple manner one assumes in an elementary circuits or electronics course. For example, a 100-ohm resistor is never exactly 100 ohms, but may have a value that varies over a range from about

90 to 110 ohms. The same is true of the parameter values for electronic devices. For example, the beta of a transistor has a certain tolerance associated with it.

In a paper design one often uses worst case analysis, where parameter values are set at the appropriate extreme of the tolerance ranges (that is, at the end of the range that yields the worst results). Comprehensive probability analysis of circuits is complicated by nonlinear operations. As an example, suppose you know that the beta of a transistor has a certain mean value and has Gaussian (normal) distribution around the mean. To see the effects of this random distribution on an output parameter, you have to track probability distributions through each portion of the circuit. As soon as you come to a nonlinear operation, your theoretical analysis comes to an abrupt halt.

The computer opens up an exciting possibility in this area. It can randomly set parameters within the tolerance limits and run the simulation many times, compiling a family of output curves. The family of curves then can be examined to generate statistics of any output parameter. If enough simulation runs are performed, the "law of large numbers" indicates that we generate an approximation to the probability distribution of the output variables. This is the essence of Monte Carlo analysis, the name deriving from the probabilities that apply to gambling. During Monte Carlo analysis, multiple runs are performed. For each run a new circuit is generated from components whose numerical parameter values are randomly selected. The selection process is based upon user-specified parameter tolerances and specified distributions within those tolerances. The display of the outputs is in the form of both multiple superimposed curves and histograms displaying statistical data.

We begin by running a simple example and then follow up with detailed descriptions of the various functions. We abandon our differential amplifier example used so far in this tutorial, since the circuit specification does not contain any component tolerances. Instead, press the F3 function key to exit the simulation, and then unload the differential amplifier and load the schematic called CARLO.CIR from the file. The circuit is shown in Figure 73.

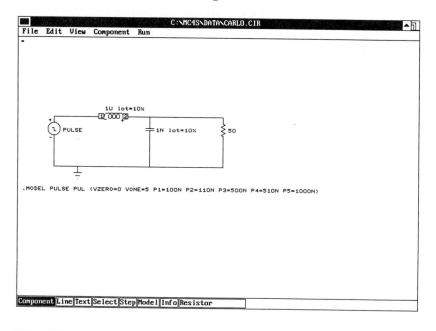

C:\MC4S\DATA\CARLO.CIR

File   Edit   View   Component   Run

1U lot=10%
1 000 2

PULSE                                1N lot=10%          50

.MODEL PULSE PUL (VZERO=0 VONE=5 P1=100N P2=110N P3=500N P4=510N P5=1000N)

Component Line Text Select Step Model Info Resistor

Figure 73

Before we printed this circuit, we selected **Show Node Numbers** from the **View** pull-down menu so that the node numbering is shown on the figure. This is needed to identify the plotted parameters, since we have not labeled the nodes with names.

If you now run the transient analysis (make sure to disable **Probe mode** from the **Run** pull-down menu if the last analysis you performed left you with a check mark next to that item), you are presented with the **Transient Analysis Limits** window, as shown in Figure 74.

Two variables are to be plotted, V(1) and V(2). Since the P entry on the **Transient Analysis Limits** window is 1 for both variables, they will be superimposed on the same set of axes, with a Y variable range of –3 to +7 volts. Also note that the M column is activated for V(2). This enables Monte Carlo

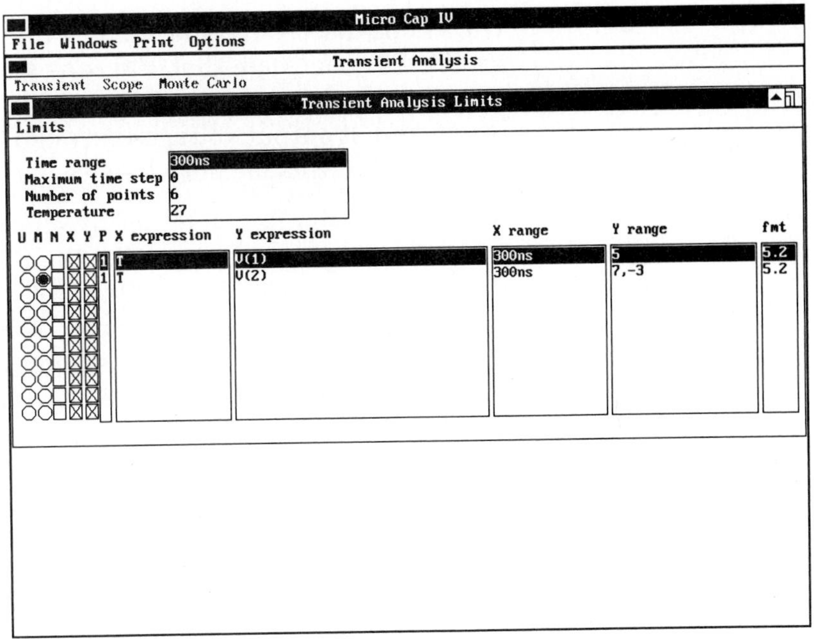

Figure 74

analysis on that variable. To see the parameters chosen for the Monte Carlo analysis, we need to pull down the **Monte Carlo options** window shown in Figure 75. Use the mouse or press Alt+**M**, and then select *1:Options*.

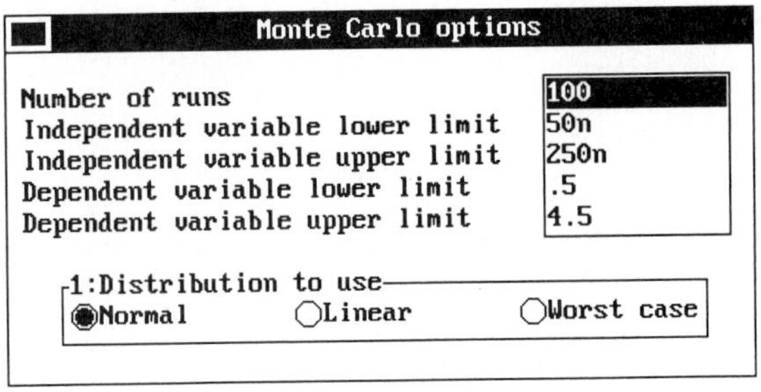

Figure 75

We will be discussing this window in detail in a few moments. For now, note that 100 runs will be performed, and we will look at a time range from 50 to 250 nanoseconds (nsec) and at output voltages between 0.5 and 4.5 volts. You will see what this means when we perform the simulation.

Activate the simulation either by selecting **Run** from the **Transient** menu or by pressing the F2 function key. The simulation runs 100 times. (On a 486 machine with a coprocessor this takes about 50 seconds. With a much slower computer, you may want to do some homework for classes while the simulation is running.) The result is shown in Figure 76. One hundred curves for V(2) are drawn superimposed on each other. Note the rectangle on the screen that defines the limits specified in the **Monte Carlo options** window of Figure 75.

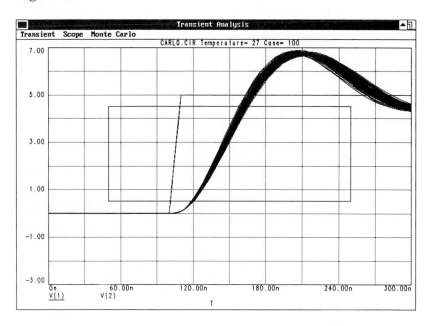

Figure 76

Now pull down the **Monte Carlo** menu and select *2:Statistics*. You see a screen similar to Figure 77.

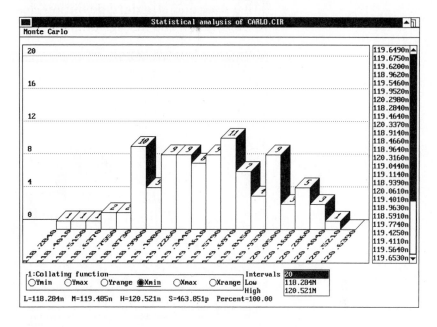

Figure 77

Don't panic if the histogram appears to be missing. You probably will find that the **Collating function** at the bottom is selected as *Ymin*. The minimum value of the Y variable within our defined box in Figure 76 is 0.5 volt for each of the 100 runs, so there is no distribution to plot. Use your mouse to select *Xmin* from **Collating function**, and the histogram of Figure 77 results. The numbers at the top of each bar represent the percentage of results falling in the corresponding range (with 100 runs it is also the number of outcomes). What is plotted is the distribution of minimum time values within the defined box. This is the distribution of times at which the waveform crosses 0.5 volt. The range is from 118.284 nsec to 120.639 nsec. The tallest bar tells us that 11% of the results fell between 119.579 nsec and 119.697 nsec. One hundred runs is not sufficient to develop the true probability distribution of the output. We reran this for 500 runs, with the result displayed in Figure 78. This approaches a Gaussian curve, with a mean value of about 119.5 nsec and standard deviation close to 0.5 nsec. The bar to the right of the histogram lists each outcome.

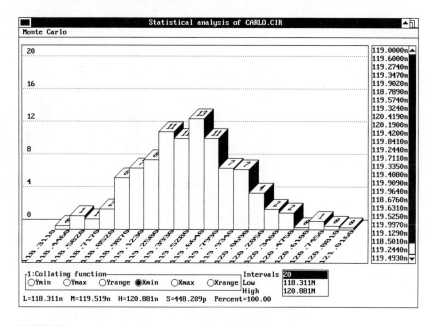

Figure 78

This concludes the simple example of Monte Carlo analysis. Now that you have experienced the excitement of this powerful tool, we take an organized look at the various functions and features.

## Tolerances

Before you can run a Monte Carlo analysis, you need to specify tolerances for the devices and components in your circuit. In the case of components, tolerances are applied to the numeric parameters (for example, ohms and farads). You can specify tolerance as an actual value or as a percentage of the nominal value.

Absolute tolerances are specified using a LOT statement. The form of specification is

**LOT=X[%]**

As an example, suppose a resistor is labeled as R1 and it is nominally a 10-kohm resistor. The tolerance is 5%. Since 5% represents an actual tolerance of 500 ohms, you have a choice of either of the following specifications for the resistor. We are using .DEFINE statements, which you place anywhere on the screen.

**.DEFINE R1 10K LOT=500** ↵

or

**.DEFINE R1 10K LOT=5%** ↵

In the case of components, you can also specify tolerances directly on the schematic as you label the parameter values. Thus, when drawing the resistor on the circuit, you could enter its value as **10K LOT=5%**.

The same approach is used to apply tolerances to device parameters. For example, suppose transistor Q1 is an NPN transistor with a nominal beta of 100 and tolerance of 20%. The .MODEL statement you type is

**.MODEL Q1 NPN (BF=100 LOT=20%)** ↵

The forward beta then ranges from 80 to 120. If several transistors are labeled Q1, the program selects a beta for each run and applies it to all Q1 transistors.

Absolute (lot) tolerance applies to all components or devices given the particular name. You can also specify a relative tolerance, where the lot tolerance, if any, is applied to all of the similarly named devices, and then the relative tolerance is applied to each individual device. To do so, you use DEV in the same way you used LOT. If only one device has the particular label, it does not matter which designation you use. Suppose, for example, that the absolute tolerance of the beta of our transistor is 10% (that is, an entire lot can be expected to have a beta between 90 and 110) and the relative tolerance is 1% (within the lot the variation is ±1% of the lot value). The .MODEL statement then reads,

**.MODEL Q1 NPN (BF=100 LOT=10% DEV=1%)** ↵

**Windowing**

Monte Carlo simulation yields a distribution of a particular parameter of the output waveform. To specify parameters, you first create a window. The analysis is performed for waveforms that pass through the window. We illustrate this concept by again referring to the example we ran earlier in this section. If you have not already done so, recall the CARLO.CIR from memory, and run the transient analysis. The result is shown in Figure 79, which is a repeat of Figure 76.

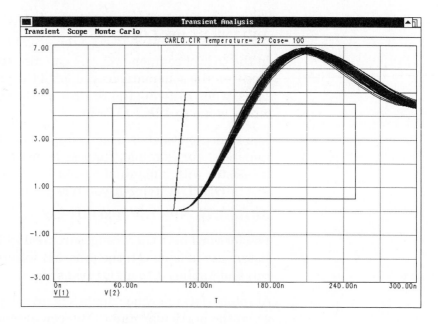

Figure 79

Our goal is to measure the rise time of the output waveform. The input is a pulse that goes from 0 to 5 volts. Let us define rise time by the 10% points (there are many definitions of rise time depending on the application). That is, we want to examine the times in which the output waveform goes from 0.5 to 4.5 volts. To do so, we define a window between these values. The vertical lines of the window are not critical, as long as they bracket all of the rise times. The window is shown on the figure as a rectangle. Our analysis would yield the same results if we narrowed the rectangle (by reducing the horizontal width). You sometimes use the vertical sides of the window to define an acceptable region, and then use the data generated by the simulation to see how many times the results fall outside of that window. The rectangle dimensions are specified in the **Monte Carlo options** window, which is opened by pulling down the **Monte Carlo** menu and selecting *1:Options*. The resulting window is shown in Figure 80, which is a repeat of Figure 75.

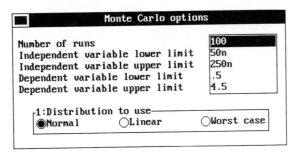

Figure 80

The first number indicates how many simulation runs are performed, while the next four entries specify the window dimensions. The remaining entry in the window is the selection of probability distribution function.

**Collating Functions**

After selecting options you are ready to display the Monte Carlo results. If you have not already done so, pull down the **Monte Carlo** menu and select *2:Statistics*. Figure 81 shows the resulting screen. The specific histogram depends on your selection of collating function. You have six possible choices, as listed at the bottom of Figure 81:

*Ymin*   Gathers the values of the Y-axis minima (within the window). As long as the monitored waveform crosses the "Dependent value lower limit," the lower limit is stored.

*Xmin*   Gathers the X values where the Y-axis minima occur.

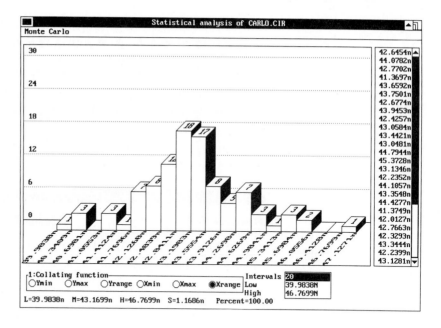

Figure 81

**Ymax**   Gathers the values of Y-axis maxima. As long as the monitored waveform crosses the "Dependent value upper limit," the upper limit is stored.

**Xmax**   Gathers the X values where the Y-axis maxima occur.

**Yrange**   Gathers the Ymax-Ymin value for each run.

**Xrange**   Gathers the Xmax-Xmin value for each run.

Note that Figure 81 illustrates a selection of **Xrange**, which is the rise time for the waveform.

### Statistical analysis window

The **Statistical analysis** window of Figure 81 contains seven regions.

The title box is at the top of the screen. The **Monte Carlo** pull-down menu is on the left of the second line. This menu has two entries:

**1:Print statistics**  Prints a statistical summary of the run to the location specified in the **Text setup** dialog box.

**2:Plot statistics**  Prepares a plotter file of the histogram display and sends it to the location specified in the **Plotter setup** dialog box.

The histogram shows the percentage of the population within each interval of the specified collating function. It occupies the largest area of the **Statistical analysis** window. The data list running along the right side of the screen is a scrollable list of the collating function values for the run.

The *1:Collating function* selector is a series of six buttons you use to select the collating function. The control box to the right of the collating buttons contains three entries:

**Intervals**  Specifies the number of histogram intervals. The example shows 20 intervals, which means the range of values is divided into 20 equal-size bins. This number specifies the number of bars in the histogram.

**High**  Sets the value above which any collating function is excluded from the percent yield.

**Low**  Sets the value below which any collating function is excluded from the percent yield.

The final area of the screen is the statistics summary, which appears across the bottom of the screen. This shows the low value (L), mean value (M), high value (H), standard deviation (S), and percent yield. Note that in our example, every collating function fell within the Low and High limits specified in the control box (100% yield).

**Probability Distributions**

The first simulation run always uses the nominal parameter values. For the remainder of the runs, the program randomly adds or subtracts a delta value to the nominal value. The probability of adding a particular delta value depends on the specified probability distribution. You can choose from three distributions on the **Monte Carlo options** window: *Worst case*, *Linear*, and *Normal* (also called Gaussian).

When you choose **Worst case** distribution, the delta value is the full tolerance value. Thus, for example, if the only circuit device with an associated tolerance were transistor Q1 with a nominal beta of 100 and tolerance of 10%, beta would take on only three values during the various simulations. The first run would set beta to the nominal value of 100; subsequent runs would use either 90 or 110 for beta. If more than one component or device has an associated tolerance, various combinations of the extreme values would occur during subsequent simulation runs.

Choose **Linear** distribution to have the value of delta uniformly distributed within the tolerance range. All values within the range are equally likely.

Choose **Normal** (or Gaussian) distribution, and the value of delta is Gaussian distributed within the tolerance range. Since the Gaussian probability density does not go identically to zero and values of delta outside the tolerance range are not permitted, we use a truncated distribution. The default value for standard deviation is the tolerance/2.58. Therefore, the extreme values represent 2.58 standard deviations away from the mean. Using this value, the delta is within the tolerance range 99% of the time. You can specify a standard deviation different from this default value by using the **Global Settings** menu. You may wish to do this if you have detailed manufacturer specifications. Suppose, for example, the supplier of the device guarantees that 95% of all resistors fall within a specified tolerance. Reference to tables of Gaussian densities (error function tables) indicate that you should set the standard deviation so that the tolerance represents 1.96 standard deviations.

Before going further, let's change the distribution from **Normal** to **Worst case**. Run the simulation, and you will get the result of Figure 82.

Although the simulation runs 100 times, only five distinct curves result. Think about this. If you examine the circuit, you find that only two components have tolerances associated with them. The inductor has a nominal value of 1 microhenry. Applying the tolerance, it has an inductance of either

CARLO.CIR Temperature= 27  Case= 100

Figure 82

0.9 uh or 1.1 uh. The capacitor has a nominal value of 1 nf, and worst case tolerance values of 0.9 or 1.1 nF. The first simulation run uses the nominal values, and all subsequent runs will set inductor values to either 0.9uh or 1.1uh, and capacitor values to 0.9 nF or 1.1 nF. Thus, following the nominal run, there are only four combinations of parameter values. This leads to a total of five curves.

# Examples

1. For the CARLO circuit, find the maximum overshoot of the pulse response. Also find the value of overshoot that is exceeded only 10% of the time.

   **Solution**: Load the CARLO.CIR circuit and perform a Monte Carlo analysis. However, instead of setting the window as you did in the tutorial (to measure rise time), set it to surround the overshoot. Set the time to run from 180 nsec to 240 nsec, and set the vertical limits to run from 6 volts to 7 volts. Run the simulation 100 times using normal distributions for the tolerances. The result of the transient analysis is illustrated in Figure 83.

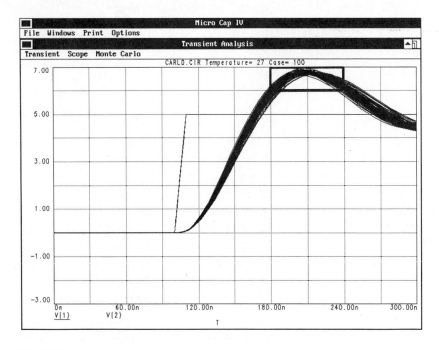

Figure 83

Figure 84 shows the statistical distribution of maximum voltage values. The maximum value of overshoot was 6.9525 volts, while 90% of the time the overshoot was below 6.8336 (simply add the percentages in the boxes on the histogram).

2. You are given the emitter follower amplifier of Figure 85.

   a. Determine the values of $V_{CEQ}$ and $I_{CQ}$.

   b. Find the maximum symmetrical output voltage swing.

   **Solution:** You begin by entering the circuit into the computer. This is done in a straightforward manner using the techniques of Tutorial #1. Note that you have alternative ways to enter the component values. For example,

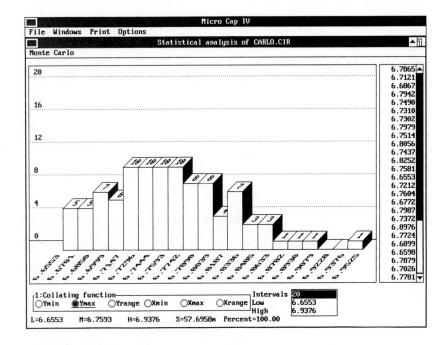

Figure 84

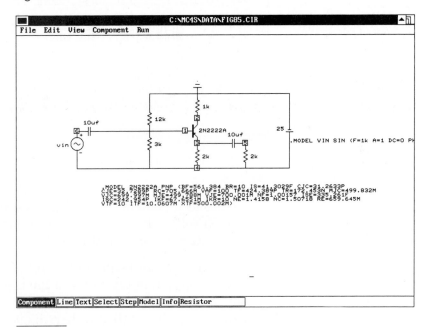

Figure 85

the 10 microfarad capacitors can be entered as 10µ, 10µF, 1E-5, or .00001.

a. You can find the quiescent values of voltage in a number of ways. Perhaps the simplest is from a transient analysis. Pull down the **Transient** menu and select *3:Options*. Then select *Operating point only*, and run the analysis. Exit the analysis by pressing the F3 function key. Finally, pull down the **View** menu and select *5:Show node voltages*. The display now looks like Figure 86.

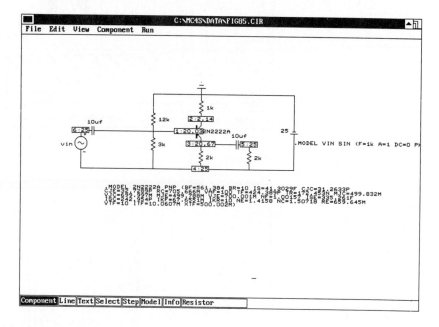

Figure 86

The collector-to-emitter voltage is simply 2.14–20.67, or –18.53 volts. The collector current is the current through the 1 kΩ resistor, and this is –2.14 mA.

b. Since this circuit is an emitter follower, the output voltage is approximately equal to the input. You can verify this by hooking any appropriate source to the input (for example, a sinusoid) and then displaying input and output waveforms. Since this circuit contains a 1 kHz sine wave as the input, you can determine the maximum output swing by stepping the amplitude of the input. After some experimentation with ranges, we stepped the input amplitude from 1 volt to 3 volts in steps of 0.25 volts. To do so, select **Stepping** from the **Transient** pull-down menu. The parameter to step is VIN.A. The result of the stepping is shown in Figure 87.

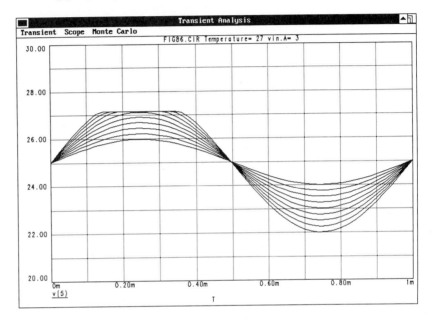

Figure 87

You see that the output starts to saturate at a voltage of about 27.15 (we reran a single curve and used the cursor mode to read this value). The maximum swing can be read as 4.9 voltage peak-to-peak. The lack of symmetry indicates that the Q-point was not placed in the middle of the load line.

3.  For the common-emitter (CE) amplifier shown in Figure 88, how much power is dissipated in the transistor?

    **Solution**: You enter the circuit component by component. Note the lack of a modifier on the capacitor values indicates 1 farad capacitors. These are not practical in a

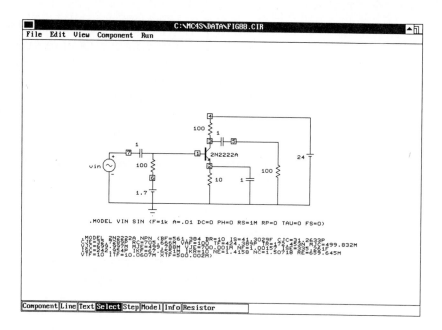

File   Edit   View   Component   Run

100 1

2N2222A

vin

100

1.7

24

100

10 1

.MODEL VIN SIN (F=1k A=.01 DC=0 PH=0 RS=1M RP=0 TAU=0 FS=0)

.MODEL 2N2222A NPN (BF=561.384 BR=10 IS=41.3029F CJC=31.2633P
CJE=264.669P RC=705.666M VAF=100 TF=424.389P TR=172.453N MJC=499.832M
CJE=264.997M MJE=499.288M VJE=700.001M NF=1.00157 ISE=325.661F
ISC=242.454P IKF=62.6488M IKR=10 NE=1.4158 NC=1.50718 RE=659.645M
VTF=10 ITF=10.0607M XTF=500.002M)

Component Line Text Select Step Model Info Resistor

Figure 88

real-life circuit, but the large value assures that they act as short circuits for the ac components of the signal.

The power dissipated in the collector-emitter is approximately equal to the total power dissipated in the transistor. You can display this directly on the transient analysis plot by specifying V(3,2)*I(4,3) as the Y expression on the **Transient Analysis Limits** window. You are therefore specifying the collector current as that from node 4 to node 3 (through the 100 Ω resistor). The voltage is the voltage between nodes 3 and 2, the collector and emitter. The resulting plot is shown in Figure 89.

The average power is approximately 1.235 watts, while the peak power is 1.26 watts. The specifications for this transistor provide for a maximum power dissipation of 0.5 watts at 25 degrees Celsius ambient air temperature, and 1.8 watts at a maximum case temperature of 25 degrees Celsius. Therefore, with the choice of resistors in this circuit, you would have to provide a heat sink if you did not want to exceed the specifications of this transistor.

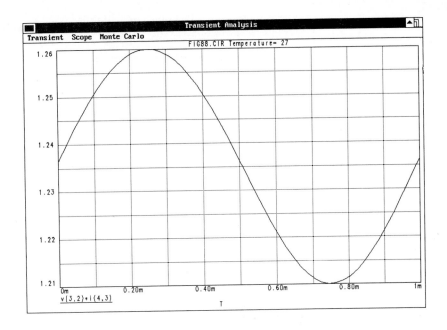

Figure 89

4. For the CE amplifier shown in Figure 88, determine the variation of voltage amplification if beta varies from 50 to 150.

**Solution**: You have already entered the circuit, and there is no need to redraw it. You simply select the stepping mode, and when asked "Step What?" enter **2N2222A.BF**. We have chosen to step beta from 50 to 150 in steps of 50. The resulting input and output waveforms are shown in Figure 90. We have also plotted the gain, $-v(5)/v(7)$. Note that this ratio is fairly constant except as the two waveforms approach zero. At these very small values, slight variations in capacitor voltages can have extreme effects on the ratio. In fact, you can see the ratio increasing rapidly as the right edge of the plot is reached. If you set the Y range of the gain at **auto**, the vertical scale will cover such a wide range that you will not be able to read the gain values. We have set this range to 50, and used the default of **auto** for all other ranges.

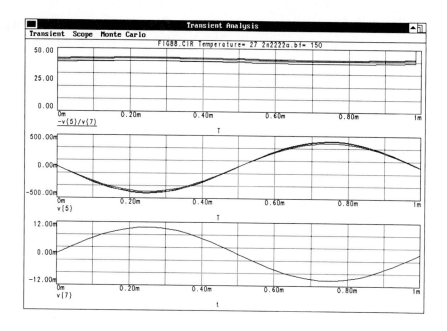

Figure 90

The gain can be read directly from the top plot. It ranges from about 40 to about 44 for the three values of beta: 50, 100, and 150.

5. Find the output waveform for the circuit shown in Figure 91, where the source is sinusoidal with an amplitude of 5 volts and a frequency of 100 Hz.

   **Solution**: You enter the circuit component by component. Note that O1 is an op-amp with default parameters. Run the transient analysis. The result is the plot shown in Figure 92. The output of the circuit is a rectified inverted version of the input.

6. You want the circuit of Figure 93 to operate as a full-wave rectifier with a gain of 1 for negative inputs and a gain of 3 for positive inputs. You solve the necessary equations and obtain the resistor values shown in the circuit of Figure 93. Another student in your class has solved the same problem and obtained the same circuit, except that $R_F$, the feedback resistor for the second

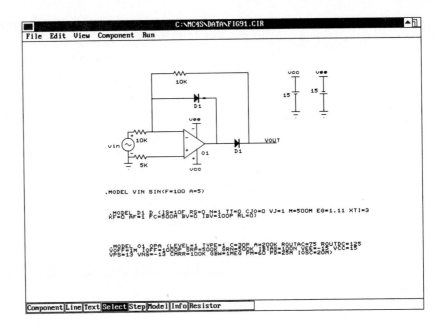

Figure 91

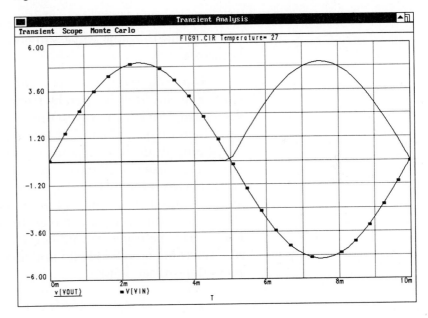

Figure 92

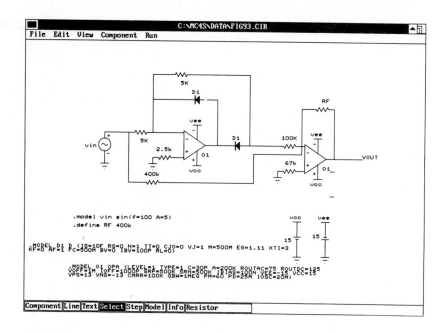

Figure 93

op-amp, is 350 kΩ. Your teacher has asked you to simulate the response to a sine wave and determine which solution is correct.

**Solution**: You enter the circuit component by component. You can find the gain by feeding in any appropriate waveform. [An easier way to find gain is to use dc analysis, which we describe in Tutorial #4.] We have chosen a 5-volt amplitude 100-Hz sinusoid, as in the previous example. You use the stepping mode to step the feedback resistor between 350 kΩ. and 400 kΩ. Perform a transient analysis and plot output and input on one set of axes, and the ratio on the other set of axes, to obtain the result of Figure 94. The upper output curve is generated for a resistor value of 400 kΩ and is clearly the one that represents the correct gains.

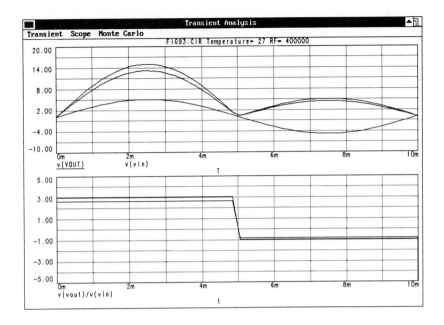

Figure 94

# Problems

1. In Tutorial #1 you were asked to design a circuit to produce an AM waveform,

   $$\sin (2\pi \times 1000t)\sin (2\pi \times 10^6 t)$$

   Plot the time waveform for $0<t<5 \times 10^{-3}$.

2. You have carefully designed the amplifier shown in Figure 50 (see Tutorial #1) to have a low temperature sensitivity. The circuit must operate between 20 and 40°C. The response to a 1 mV pulse must not exceed 5 volts at any time, since this is driving an A/D and you do not want to saturate. Use a simulation to find the best value for R2.

3. Find the range of quiescent collector currents for the amplifier shown in Figure 51 (see Tutorial #1). The transistor beta varies from 300 to 400, and the temperature varies from $-50°$ to $+65°C$.

$R_1 = R_2 = 4 \text{ k}\Omega$
$R_E = 50 \ \Omega$
$R_L = R_C = 1 \text{ k}\Omega$

Now let the input be a sinusoid of amplitude A. Find the maximum value of A before there is visible distortion in the output. Repeat for $R_E = 100 \ \Omega$.

4. A 1-kHz square wave forms the input to the circuit of Figure 52 (see Tutorial #1). Plot the output waveform.

5. Experiment with the following circuits, which are stored on your disk. When you execute the transient analysis using the stored limits, you will experience many of the functions available for MICRO-CAP IV.

**FFT1.CIR** A circuit that demonstrates selected Fourier transforms signal-processing functions.

**GILBERT.CIR** An analog multiplier circuit.

**GUMMEL.CIR** Shows the nonlinear curves in the Gummel-Poon transistor model.

**L1.CIR** Illustrates the equivalent between a circuit and a LaPlace source with the same transfer function.

**OPAMP1.CIR** Illustrates the differences between the three levels of op-amp modeling.

**SWITCH.CIR** Illustrates the operation of the three types of switches.

**TL1.CIR** Demonstrates a transmission line. Note that vap is the positive input voltage, vam is the negative input voltage, and vbp and vbm are positive and negative output voltages, respectively.

**F1.CIR** Shows the use of the VCO macro within a circuit. This generates a varying frequency output. Note that it uses VCO.CIR, which is a macro stored on your disk.

# 3

---

# AC Analysis

---

## Introduction

AC analysis provides a means of evaluating the small-signal transfer characteristics of a circuit. If the circuit contains any nonlinear elements, the program calculates the dc operating point to determine the small-signal characteristics of each nonlinear element. The element is then replaced with a linear element representing these small-signal characteristics.

The circuit must contain one or more independent (waveform) sources. The simulation replaces pulse, sine, and user sources with fixed 1-volt amplitude ac signals. Circuits containing SPICE independent sources (V and I) already have user-specified ac signal amplitudes. The analysis is performed using complex phasor quantities. Since the phasors are complex, the program performs specified operations on the output in order to present plots. These operators include real, imaginary, dB, magnitude, phase, and group delay. In addition to plotting voltages and currents as a function of frequency, the program can also produce Nyquist diagrams.

A Nyquist diagram is a plot of the imaginary part of the output versus the real part of the output.

Begin by drawing a circuit, either by entering each component, as described in Tutorial #1 or by retrieving a network from the data file. If you already have a circuit in the **Schematic Editor** window, unload it using the **File** menu. Although you may use any circuit you have created, we illustrate ac analysis for the TUTOR1 circuit. Retrieve this by pulling down the **File** menu, selecting *3:Load Schematic*, and then scrolling to TUTOR1.CIR (recall that you can skip to the first "T" entry by typing **T**). Your screen should look like Figure 95, which is similar to the PRLC circuit used in the example of Part I of this manual. The only significant changes are the parameters of the pulse source, and these do not affect ac analysis.

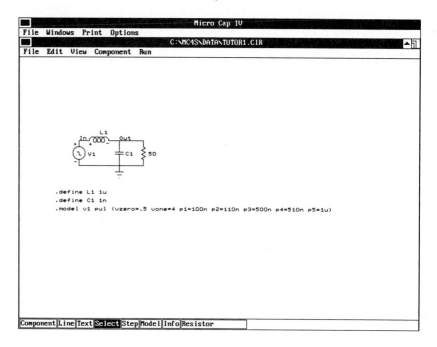

Figure 95

Once the network is on the screen, the analysis is initiated by pulling down the **Run** menu and selecting *2:AC analysis.* Alternatively, you can use the keyboard in one of two ways. Either type the menu identifier followed by the entry

**R; 2**

or use the hotkey (identified on the pull-down menu) by simply pressing Alt+**2**.

After you initiate ac analysis, you are presented with the **AC Analysis Limits** window. We begin this tutorial with a discussion of this window. We then discuss each of the menus available in the ac analysis.

# AC Analysis Limits

After activating the ac analysis, you are presented with the **AC Analysis Limits** window, which shows 16 limits used in the analysis. When you store a circuit, the limits are stored with it. If you create a new circuit, default limits are used. The limits stored in the TUTOR1 circuit are shown in Figure 96.

We now describe each of these analysis limits. However, if you are impatient to see an analysis run, you can simply pull down the **AC** menu (using the mouse, or by pressing Alt+**A**) and select *Run* (or press the F2 function key).

**Numeric Limits Fields**

The upper portion of the window contains a field with six entries.

### Frequency Range

The format for this is

**fmax[,fmin]**

The analysis starts at fmin and ends at **fmax**. If you omit fmin, it defaults to fmax, and the analysis is performed at a single point. Negative frequency values are not allowed.

If you perform an analysis at a single frequency, the output plot contains only one point. In fact, when you look at the

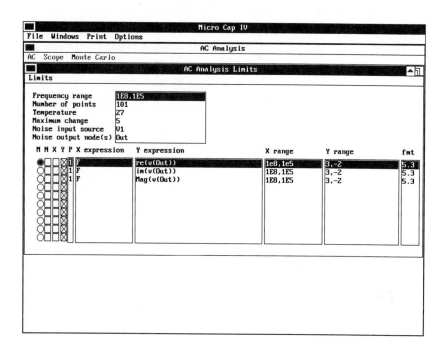

Figure 96

graph, you may think it is blank. You can read the value at this single frequency point in two convenient ways. You can specify numeric output in the **Limits** menu, or you can use the cursor mode after the simulation is run. If you select *2:Cursor mode* from the **Scope** pull-down menu, the cursor immediately positions itself at the single frequency point, and you can read out the values.

### Number of Points

There is no interpolation in ac analysis (as there is in transient analysis), so the points calculated are the same as the points printed. The frequency values at which the calculation is performed depends on the selection you make in the **Options** window (we discuss this window shortly): You can select either *Auto, Fixed linear step,* or *Fixed log step.*

If you select *Auto*, the number of points is controlled by the *Maximum change* value. We discuss this when we examine the *Maximum change* selection.

If you select either *Fixed linear step* or *Fixed log step*, the *Number of points* entry in the **AC Analysis Limits** window determines the selected frequencies. For fixed linear steps, the frequency step size is

**(fmax–fmin)/(number of points–1)**

For fixed log steps, the frequency step is

**(fmax/fmin)**$^{1/(\text{number of points}-1)}$

The default value for the number of points is 51.

### Temperature

Temperature enters into the parameter equations for devices and components. One or more temperature values (in degrees Celsius) can be specified for the analysis. The format is

**High [,Low[,Step]]**

The square brackets indicate you can omit Step, or you can omit both Low and Step. The default value for Low is High while the default value for Step is the difference between High and Low. Therefore, if only one value is specified, the simulation runs at that temperature. If two values are specified, the simulation runs at those two values, the Low and High temperatures. For example, enter **27, 25** to run the simulation twice at 25 and 27 degrees Celsius (27 degrees is room temperature). An entry of **35,20,5** runs the simulation at 20, 25, 30, and 35 degrees.

### Maximum Change

If you select the *Auto* option from the *Frequency step* menu on the **Options** window, the program automatically adjusts the frequency step up and down during the analysis. The maximum change you enter is a percentage. If the plot values change by more than this percent of full scale, the system reduces the step size. Typical *Maximum change* values needed to produce smooth curves range from 1 to 5 percent.

### Noise Input Source

This field is used to specify the name of the source where input noise is calculated. The field applies only to the calculation of Inoise and Onoise variables.

### Noise Output Node(s)

This field is used to specify the node at which output noise is calculated. The format is

**Node1[,Node2]**

Two nodes separated by a comma specify a differential output noise voltage. This field applies only if Inoise or Onoise variables are calculated.

**Waveform Options Fields**

We now turn our attention to the wide table occupying the lower half of the **AC Analysis Limits** window of Figure 96. The table contains ten columns, five of which are waveform options. Each of these is described below.

### M

The M (Monte Carlo) radio button is enabled if you want to perform a Monte Carlo analysis. Only one waveform can be selected for Monte Carlo analysis (that is, there can be only one dark button in the entire M column).

### N

The N (Numeric) column is in the form of a toggle box. It is used to select waveforms for numeric output. Numeric output is directed to a parallel or serial port, to the screen, or to a file, depending on the selection made in the **Printer setup for text** window.

### X

This toggle box determines whether the X variable is linear or logarithmic. An X in the box indicates linear, while the absence of an X indicates the scale will be a log scale.

## Y

This toggle box is the same as **X,** except it is for the Y variable.

## P

When several variables are plotted, we have a choice of superimposing them on the same set of axes or having them appear on separate, nonoverlapping graphs. The numeric entry in the P column is a number from 1 to 9. This indicates to which group the particular waveform is assigned. If you use the same number for several rows, these waveforms are plotted on the same set of axes. If the ranges are not the same, the plot uses the union of the individual ranges. You should exercise caution in plotting dissimilar variables on the same set of axes. MICRO-CAP IV does not track the units in its calculations. If, for example, you plot a gain that runs from 0 to 10 dB on the same set of axes as a phase that ranges from 0 to 360 degrees, the gain curve only occupies a small portion of the range.

The example of Figure 96 generates three curves plotted on one set of axes. If we wanted the curves on separate plots, we would assign different P numbers to them. Note that we are not currently plotting either noise parameter. We examine noise later in this tutorial.

## Expression Fields

The remaining five columns relate to the expressions to be plotted.

### X Expression

This field specifies the expressions for the X-axis variable. In most cases this is a frequency variable. One notable exception is a Nyquist plot, where the X expression is the real part of the output. An example of a Nyquist plot is given in the examples at the end of this tutorial.

## Y Expression

This field specifies the expressions for the Y-axis variables. Since the program operates with complex phasors, complex operators are used. You can choose from among the following operators, where X is a labeled voltage or a variable such as V(A,B):

**RE(X)**    Real part of X

**IM(X)**    Imaginary part of X

**MAG(X)** Magnitude of X

**PH(X)**    Phase of X in degrees

**GD(X)**    Group delay = rate of change of phase with (radian) frequency

You can also plot mathematical functions of these operators, such as dB(MAG(X)) for a decibel plot of the magnitude.

If you plot the phase of a variable, the plot begins at the second analysis point. This delay occurs because of an algorithm written into the program that removes phase ambiguity. It must compare the second point to the first before establishing a phase reference. If you need the exact phase at a particular frequency, start the analysis below that frequency.

## X Range

This sets the scale ranges for the X waveforms. The format is

**High[,Low]**

In our example, we run the simulation from 100 kHz to 100 MHz, so the entry is **1E8, 1E5** for the X range. The default for Low is zero.

Caution: Do not use the default value for Low if you are plotting X on a log scale. If you do so, you receive an error message.

You can enter **auto** for this field, and MICRO-CAP IV automatically sets the range using the designated frequency range. Place the cursor on the appropriate field and type

**auto**, or for a faster way, use the **Limits** menu, as discussed in the next section.

### Y Range

This field is the same as X range, except it is for the Y variable. You can enter **auto**, and MICRO-CAP IV automatically sets the range to fill the screen after running the simulation.

### fmt

This field controls the format of printed numbers used in the tabular printout or the cursor mode. The number to the left of the decimal point sets the space for digits to the left of the decimal point in the printed numbers. Similarly, the number to the right of the decimal point sets the number of digits to the right of the decimal point. The example shows 5.3, which means printouts will contain up to five digits to the left of the decimal point and three to the right (that is, thousandths).

**Limits Pull-Down Menu**

In the upper-left-hand corner of the **AC Analysis Limits** window is the **Limits** pull-down menu. The **Limits** menu contains two entries: ***Default all*** and ***Default blank***. If you select ***Default all***, the program inserts "auto" into all range fields with valid plot numbers. If you select ***Default blank***, the program inserts "auto" into all *blank* range fields with valid plot numbers.

**Running the Analysis**

Once you are satisfied with the ac analysis limits, you are ready to run the analysis. Run the analysis by pulling down the **AC** menu (with the mouse or by pressing Alt+**A**) and clicking ***1:Run***. You can save all this work by simply pressing the F2 function key. The ac analysis is produced, as shown in Figure 97.

As in the case of other types of analyses, you can exert two types of immediate control on the simulation as it is running: You can terminate the simulation by pressing the Esc key, and if you press **P** during the run, you toggle a numeric

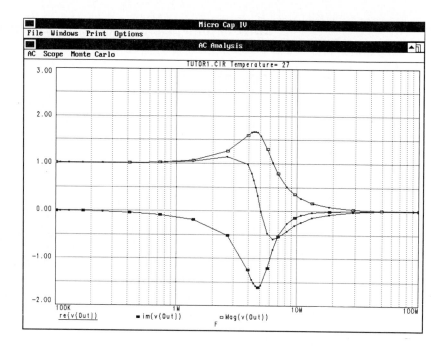

Figure 97

display. This display shows the X and Y expression values during the simulation run.

The three curves appear in different colors on a color computer monitor. Before producing the printout of Figure 97, we added tokens to the drawing using the **Options** window selection. This was described in Tutorial #2, and we discuss it again in a few moments.

Below the title bar for the **AC Analysis** window (Figure 97) are three pull-down menus: **AC**, **Scope**, and **Monte Carlo**. We now discuss each of these.

## AC Menu

Once you select *2:AC analysis* from the **Run** menu, you can pull down the **AC** menu either with the mouse (after clearing the **AC Analysis Limits** window by pressing the Esc key) or by pressing Alt+**A**. The menu contains six selections.

> 1:Run
> 2:Limits
> 3:Options
> 4:Stepping
> 5:Numeric output
> 6:Plot analysis

## 1:Run

You select this menu entry to run the simulation.

## 2:Limits

This option opens the **AC Analysis Limits** window so you can change limits. The **AC Analysis Limits** window is automatically opened when you select *AC analysis* from the **Run** menu, so you access this from the **AC** menu only if you wish to make changes following a simulation run.

## 3:Options

Clicking on *3:Options* presents the **AC options** window, as shown in Figure 98. This window is divided into three areas: *1:Run options*, *3:Frequency step*, and *Other options*. Selections may be made by clicking the mouse on the appropriate button or box. You can leave the options window either by initiating the run (pull down **AC** menu with the mouse or by pressing Alt+**A** and select *Run*), by erasing the window (click on the box to the left of the title), or by pressing the Esc key.

### 1:Run options

This area offers you three choices. *Normal* produces a normal run. *Save* saves the entire simulation for later retrieval. *Retrieve* retrieves a saved simulation for review.

### 3:Frequency step

You have three choices for controlling the frequency step. If you select *Auto*, the frequency steps are calculated automatically based on the rate of change of the first waveform. If the rate of change varies from one solution to the next by more

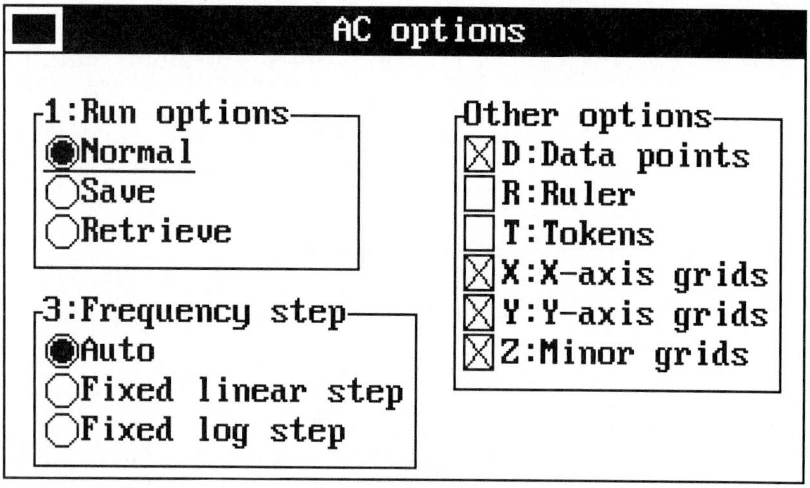

```
┌────────────────────────────────────────────────┐
│ ■            AC options                         │
├────────────────────────────────────────────────┤
│  ┌1:Run options──────┐   ┌Other options──────┐ │
│  ●Normal                 ⊠D:Data points        │
│  ○Save                   □R:Ruler              │
│  ○Retrieve               □T:Tokens             │
│  └───────────────────┘   ⊠X:X-axis grids       │
│                          ⊠Y:Y-axis grids       │
│  ┌3:Frequency step───┐   ⊠Z:Minor grids        │
│  ●Auto                   └───────────────────┘ │
│  ○Fixed linear step                            │
│  ○Fixed log step                               │
│  └───────────────────┘                         │
└────────────────────────────────────────────────┘
```

Figure 98

than *Maximum change* (specified in the **AC Analysis Limits** window), the frequency step is reduced. Otherwise it is increased.

If you select either *Fixed linear step* or *Fixed log step*, the frequencies are stepped by an amount specified by the number of points. We discussed the actual step size earlier when we examined the **Limits** window.

### Other Options

This portion of the **AC options** menu contains six entries. These are the same as those in the **Transient options** menu.

**Data points**  Causes the actual data points of the simulation to be marked on the plot.

**Ruler**  Selects ruler marks in lieu of full screen graph divider lines.

**Tokens**  Adds a token to all but the first waveform of each group. The token also appears on the corresponding axis scale to help in the identification process.

**X-Axis grids**  Draws vertical grids or rule marks.

**Y-Axis grids**  Draws horizontal grids or rule marks.

**Minor log grids**  Used to switch the minor log grids (between powers of 10) on and off. It applies only to logarithmic scales.

**4:Stepping**

Component parameters may be stepped from one value to another, producing multiple runs with multiple output waveforms. You activate this feature by selecting *4:Stepping* from the **AC** menu and then entering instructions in the dialog box. The dialog box for this example is shown in Figure 99.

The stored parameters for this example do not include any stepping, so the entries are blank.

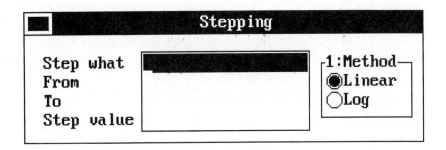

Figure 99

### Step What

This is where you specify which parameter you want to change. To step the value of a component, you enter the name of that component. For example, if you named one or more resistors R1, you would enter **R1** to step their values.

In the case of stepping device parameters, you enter the device name, a period, and the parameter you want to vary.

**Limits**

*From* specifies the starting value of the parameter. *To* specifies the ending value of the parameter. *Step value* specifies the amount by which to step the parameter.

**5:Numeric Output**

If you have placed an X in the **N** column of the **AC Analysis Limits** menu, the numeric output is displayed as soon as you run the simulation. The display is in a window in front of the graphical output plots. You can remove the numeric window by pressing the Esc key. Once the window is removed, you can again activate it by selecting *5:Numeric output* from the **AC** menu.

**6:Plot Analysis**

This command generates output to a plotter or file according to the instructions in the Plotter setup dialog box. The option is selected after the analysis is complete. The same waveforms plotted on the screen are then sent to the plotter or to the file.

## Scope Menu

The **Scope** pull-down menu is used to select various scope commands. The menu provides you with 11 choices. The menu selections and operation are identical whether you are performing a transient, ac, or dc analysis. Therefore, we will not repeat the menu description and instead refer you to Tutorial #2.

Figure 100 shows the scope display for the TUTOR1 circuit, where we have used the scope to find the peak of the output magnitude curve. We have placed both cursors at the peak of the magnitude curve. To do so, we selected *High* from the selections at the bottom, positioned the cursor using the appropriate mouse button, and then pressed the arrow keys to move the left cursor to the peak and the Shift+arrow keys to

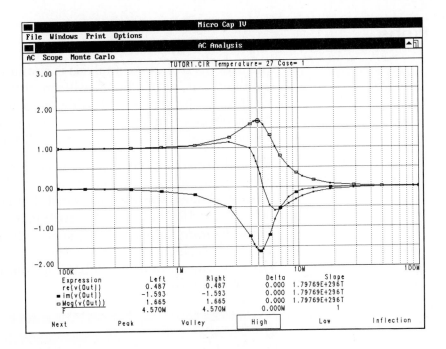

Figure 100

move the right cursor. Note that the peak occurs at the frequency of 4.57 MHz and has a value of 1.665.

When we discussed the cursor functions in Tutorial #2, our example only contained one waveform. Here we have three waveforms. How does the cursor know which of the three highs to locate? In fact, in all modes except next, the operation applies to the selected waveform. The selected waveform is the one that is underlined in the Expression column below the graph. To change the selection, we positioned the cursor on the desired expression name and clicked the left mouse button. Alternatively, we could have used the Tab key to select waveforms. This can be done either in the **AC Analysis** window (before selecting the *Scope* option), or after the scope mode is displayed.

# Probe

The PROBE tool for ac analysis is similar to that for transient analysis, with a few significant differences. Before reading this section you should study the "PROBE" section in Tutorial #2 (which discusses transient analysis), since here we discuss only those areas that are different.

We shall illustrate the ac probe mode for the DIFFAMP.CIR example. If you have a different circuit in the **Schematic Editor** window, you should unload that circuit and load the DIFFAMP.CIR. Pull down the **Run** menu, and select *4:Probe mode*, unless a check is already next to that item (there will be a check if your previous run used probe mode). Then run the ac analysis. You are presented with the split screen of Figure 101.

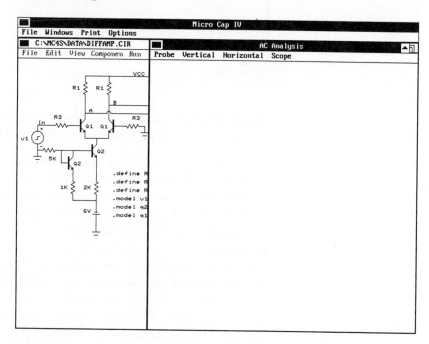

Figure 101

Pull down the **Vertical** menu in the **AC Analysis** window. It contains three categories of variables. These are *not* the same as those in a transient probe analysis. You get to choose the variable to be plotted on the vertical axis—voltage, current, noise input or output, or frequency. You also get to choose an operator, since the variables in ac analysis are complex. You can choose magnitude, dB magnitude, phase, group delay, or real or imaginary part. Finally, you get to select whether you want the vertical axis to be log or linear. Unless you want to plot a Nyquist diagram, the horizontal variable normally is frequency.

Suppose you select *Voltage, Magnitude (dB)*, and *Linear* for the vertical axis. Then click the cursor at two different points on the diagram: the node labeled A and the node labeled OutA. We can keep adding plots up to a total of six since we have selected *5:Many traces* from the **Probe** menu (see Tutorial #2). The result is shown in Figure 102. We have used the *Options* selection on the **Probe** menu to place tokens on the multiple plots.

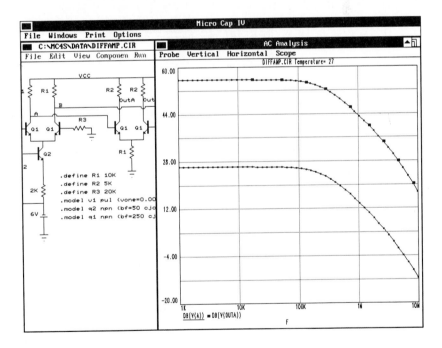

Figure 102

Note that the **Scope** pull-down menu is available to manipulate the curves and to read values using the cursors. This is operated in the same manner as when we are not in the probe mode.

You can remove the last curve or all of the curves by selecting *2:Remove* or *3:Remove all* from the **Probe** menu. To remove all curves, you also can use the hotkey by pressing the F9 function key.

## Monte Carlo Analysis

The operation of Monte Carlo Analysis is identical whether you are performing a transient, AC, or DC analysis. We therefore do not repeat the detailed discussion of Tutorial #2.

We perform one example to illustrate the process. Unload the TUTOR1 circuit, and load the CARLO circuit. Your screen should look like Figure 103.

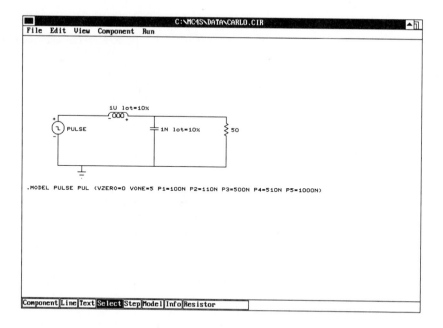

Figure 103

The circuit is a lowpass filter with tolerances assigned to the inductor and capacitor. Select *2:AC analysis* from the **Run** menu, and the **AC Analysis Limits** window is displayed, as shown in Figure 104. When you pull down the **Run** menu, make sure that *Probe mode* is not checked (it is if your last simulation used this option). If it is checked, select it to remove the check.

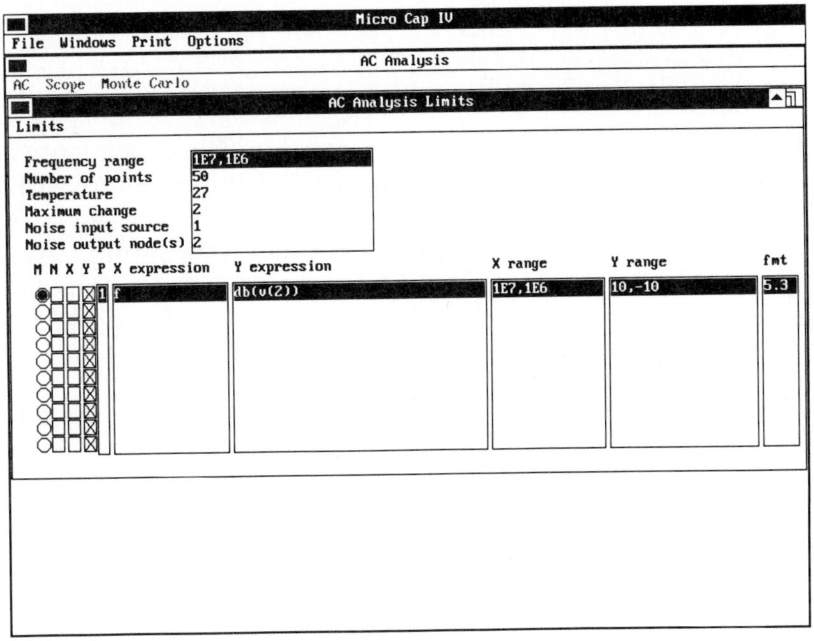

Figure 104

Note that the M column has an activated bubble in the db(V(2)) row, so we are ready to run a Monte Carlo analysis. To set the parameters, pull down the **Monte Carlo** menu with the mouse or by pressing Alt+**M**. Then select *1:Options* to display the **Monte Carlo options** window, shown in Figure 105.

The numbers stored in the file produce a Monte Carlo analysis with 100 runs. The window is defined as running between 2 MHz and 9 MHz, and from –3 to +7 on the

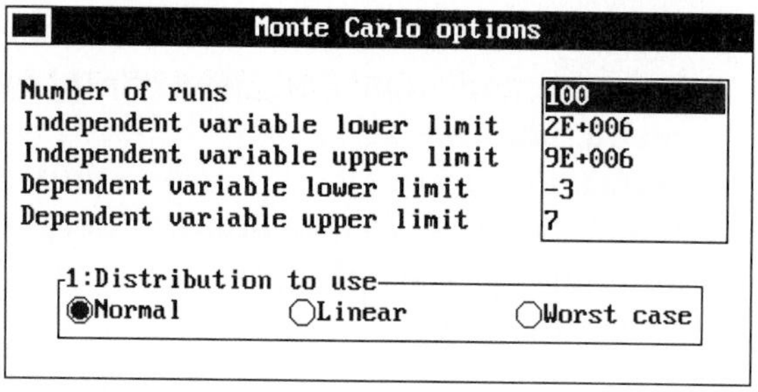

```
  ■■                Monte Carlo options
  Number of runs                             100
  Independent variable lower limit           2E+006
  Independent variable upper limit           9E+006
  Dependent variable lower limit             -3
  Dependent variable upper limit             7

     ┌1:Distribution to use───────────────────────────
     ●Normal          ○Linear          ○Worst case
```

Figure 105

dependent variable. The dependent variable (selected from the **AC Analysis Limits** menu) is **db(v(2))**, which is the output voltage. Since ac analysis substitutes a 1-volt sinusoidal source for the input, this output variable is the same as the transfer function. That is, you could have asked the program to plot **db(v(2)/v(1))**, and the result would not have been any different. (Don't take our word for it–try it!)

When you run the simulation (press the F2 function key), the result shown in Figure 106 is produced.

By defining the window to have a lower edge at –3 dB, you can use the Monte Carlo analysis to examine the roll off of the filter, in particular the statistics of the 3-dB cutoff of the filter.

Pull down the **Monte Carlo** menu and select *2:Statistics*. Since you want the statistics of the frequency at which the –3-dB magnitude level is crossed, select *Xmin.* Recall that this gathers the X values where the Y-axis minima occur. The result is shown in Figure 107.

The mean value of 3-dB cutoff is 7.27 MHz. The histogram shows the statistics of this cutoff frequency. Suppose, for example, you were designing this filter and wanted the cutoff to be below 7.5 MHz. The distribution shows that about 10% of the time (3+2+1+1+2+1), this specification is not met. If this is unacceptable, you might specify lower tolerance components (at higher cost).

Figure 106

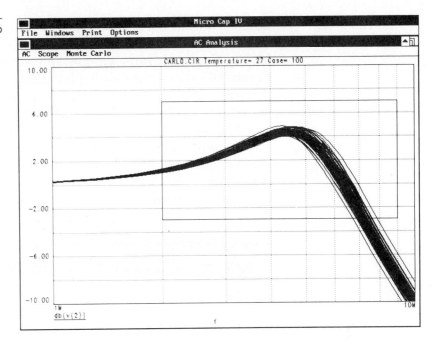

Figure 107

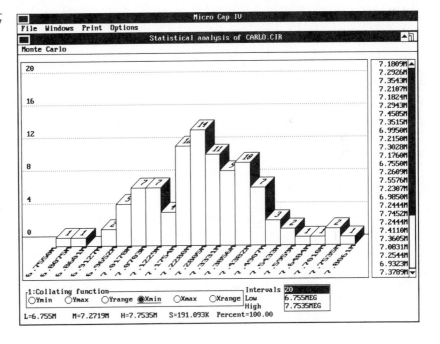

Let's rerun this using worst case distributions for the two elements (inductor and capacitor). Select **Worst case** from the **Monte Carlo options** window and run the simulation. Figure 108 shows the result. Note that instead of 100 curves, there are only five representing the nominal component values and the four combinations of extreme tolerances. The resulting Monte Carlo distribution is shown in Figure 109. The bar with "1" in the center represents the first simulation run using the nominal values. The reason that the other four bars are not the same height is that the process uses random numbers. If we ran this many more times, we would expect the four bars to be of equal height.

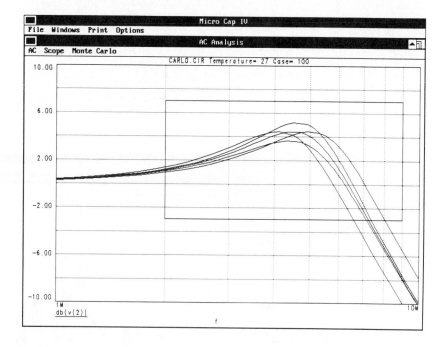

Figure 108

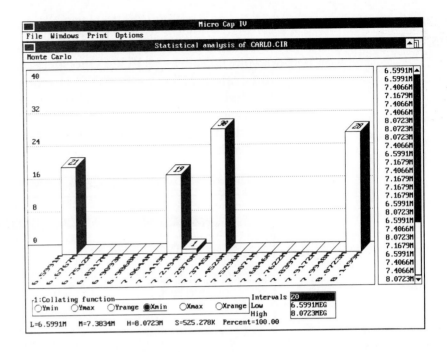

Figure 109

# Noise

MICRO-CAP IV models three types of noise: thermal, shot, and flicker noise. Thermal noise is associated with resistance. This includes both discrete resistors and parasitic resistance, which is part of the active device models. Shot noise (or quantum noise) occurs since current is a discrete phenomenon resulting from electron movement. Shot noise is usually associated with dependent current sources and semiconductor devices. Flicker noise originates from a variety of sources, including contamination traps and crystal defects in BJTs.

MICRO-CAP IV performs a noise simulation that measures the contribution from all of these noise sources. To measure output noise, you need to specify the output node(s) across which the noise is measured. In our earlier discussion of the **AC Analysis Limits** window, we mentioned two items relating to noise: the noise input source and the noise output node(s). Once you specify the output nodes, you can plot the output noise by specifying Onoise as the Y expression. We illustrate this for the TUTOR1 circuit used earlier in this tutorial. Load that circuit and select *AC analysis* from the **Run** menu. Then modify the **AC Analysis Limits** window in order to plot Onoise. The modified window is shown in Figure 110.

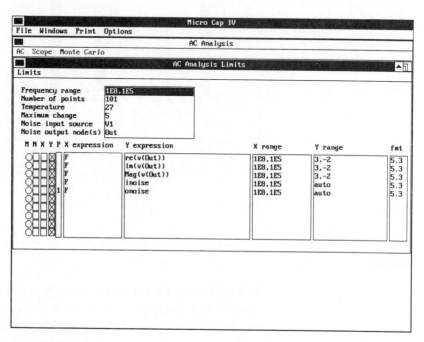

Figure 110

We have added two lines to the waveform option fields of this window. Do this by clicking the mouse on the appropriate location, or by using the up and down arrow keys and Tab key to move vertically and horizontally. Then type the entry. We have also removed the numbers from the P column for the first three curves. We could have plotted **Inoise** and **Onoise** simultaneously, but we choose to start with the output noise. Note that we have specified auto for the Y range so that the resulting plot fills the screen.

You cannot simultaneously run the noise analysis with other variables. This is true because noise analysis deals with rms values, and the equations are structured differently. If you try to plot one of the other variables at the same time as the noise, the program issues an error message.

You can now run the ac noise analysis by pressing the F2 function key. The result is shown in Figure 111. The TUTOR1 circuit contains a resistor, an inductor, and a capacitor. The only source of noise is the resistor, and it produces thermal noise. Since the noise is modeled as a random process, where the parameter of interest is mean square value, we are only interested in magnitude information. There are no phase plots associated with noise. The vertical scale for the output noise is voltage, but it is actually calculated as the square root of the mean square value.

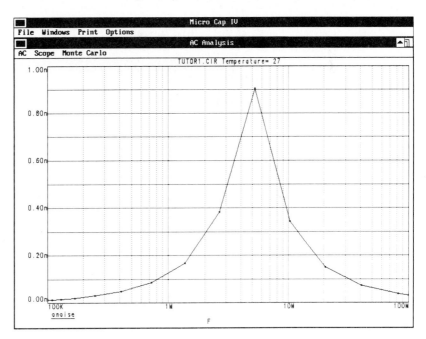

Figure 111

Input noise is calculated across the same nodes as output noise. The only difference is that the output noise is divided by the gain from the input source to the output node(s). You can think of this as the equivalent amount of noise at the input source that would produce the output noise if there were no other noise sources in the circuit. If the circuit is not frequency selective (that is, it is an allpass filter), there is no difference between input and output noise. For the circuit to know what gain to use in the calculation, you must tell it the identity of the input source. This is done in the **AC Analysis Limits** menu, as discussed earlier.

We now return to our example. Let's plot both the input and output noise and specify the input noise source to be V1 (the only source in this circuit). The **AC Analysis Limits** menu is shown in Figure 112.

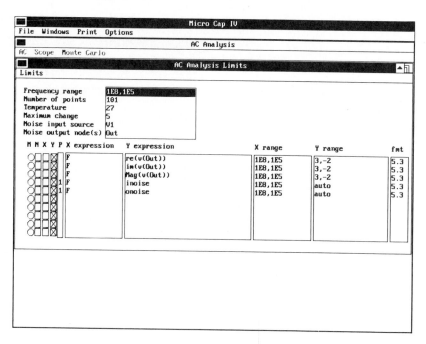

Figure 112

We run the simulation by pressing the **F2** function key, and the result is shown in Figure 113.

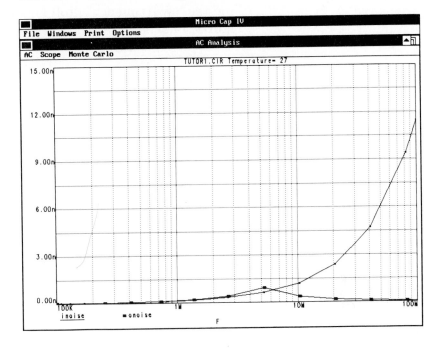

Figure 113

We have added tokens to the plot using the **Options** menu. The input noise is increasing for high frequencies because the gain is decreasing. Since we divide the output noise by the gain, the ratio increases.

# Examples

1. Find the low-frequency cutoff for the amplifier shown in Figure 114, where the beta of the transistor is 200.

Figure 114

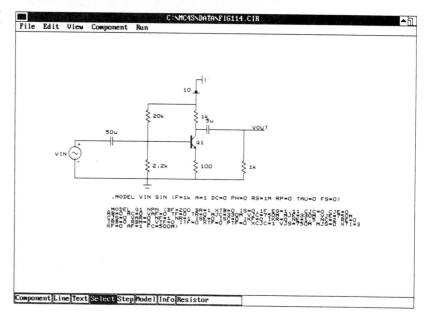

**Solution**: Input the circuit in the usual manner. Since the beta of the transistor is given as 200, we have modified the default model parameters for the NPN transistor. Although you must have a .MODEL statement for the sinusoidal source, the specific parameters do not matter since the simulation replaces this with a 1-volt variable frequency source.

Run the ac simulation to obtain the result shown in Figure 115. Note that you are plotting db(V(VOUT)). Since the problem asked for the low-frequency cutoff, you need to find the frequency at which the gain reduces by 6 dB. Use the *Cursor* option within the **Scope** menu to find this point. The right cursor is set at the flat part of the curve, and the gain is read as 12.785 dB. Then click and drag the left cursor to look for a point where the gain is as close to 6.785 dB as possible. You find this to be at a frequency of about 9 Hz.

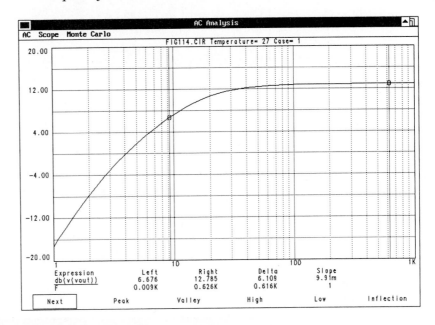

Figure 115

2.  A CD amplifier is shown in Figure 116. Determine the low-frequency cutoff of this amplifier.

    **Solution**: Input the circuit with a default .MODEL statement for the JFET. Then run the simulation, adjusting the vertical and horizontal axis limits to include the passband and the roll off. The result is shown in Figure 117. Use the cursors to find that the gain in the passband is –4.356 dB, and the gain reduces by 6 dB to –10.287 at a frequency of 1650 Hz.

3.  Describe the frequency response of a system with the following transfer function:

$$H(s) = \frac{3s^2 + 60}{s^2 + s + 20}$$

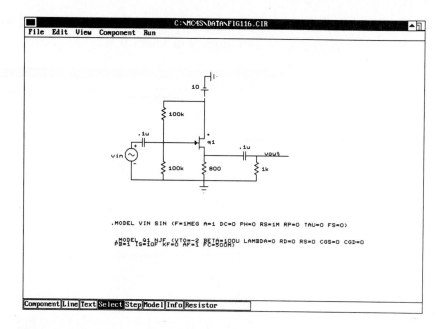

Figure 116

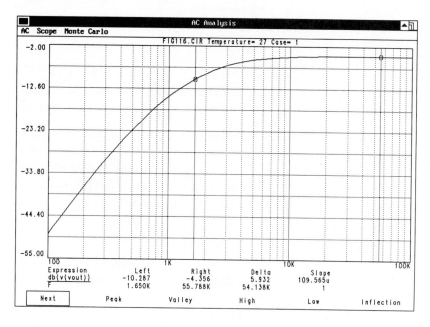

Figure 117

Figure 118

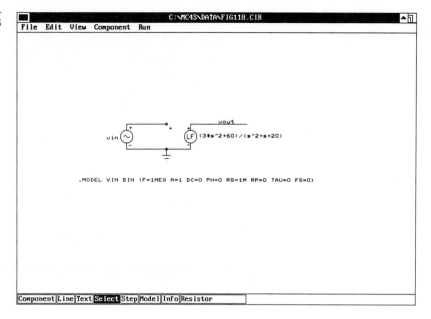

**Solution**: We use the Laplace source and the circuit shown in Figure 118 to obtain the response curve of Figure 119.

Figure 119

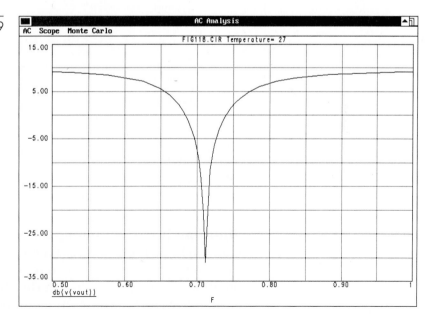

Note that we have chosen a linear horizontal axis to emphasize that the response is approximately symmetrical around a frequency of 0.71 Hz. This is a notch filter. The result agrees closely with theory, since the numerator goes to zero at a frequency of $\sqrt{20}$ radians/sec, which is approximately 0.71 Hz.

4. You are designing a first-order active filter with a dc gain of 10 and a corner frequency of 1 kHz. The circuit is shown in Figure 120, where you must choose the value of C1. Find the value of C using theory. Then use the simulation for that value, stepping on either side of it. Refine the selection with smaller steps until you find the value of C1 that achieves the specified corner frequency.

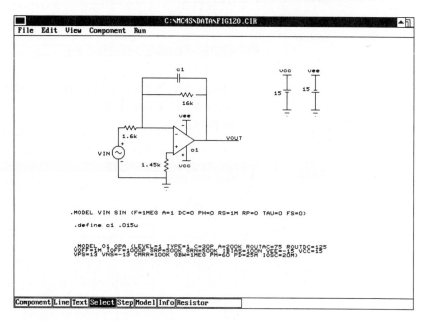

Figure 120

**Solution**: Begin by entering the circuit. A cautionary note might be helpful here. When the author first entered this circuit, he used C instead of C1 for the capacitor designation. In attempting to run the simulation, the program returned an error statement, because C is a parameter within the op-amp model, so we cannot also specify its value with a .DEFINE statement.

Use the theory to find the approximate value of C1 to be 0.015 µF. Next step C1 from 0.01 to 0.02 µF. The result is shown in Figure 121. The value of 0.017 µF yields a 6-dB point almost exactly at 1 kHz. Futher narrowing of the stepping limit confirmed this choice for the capacitor.

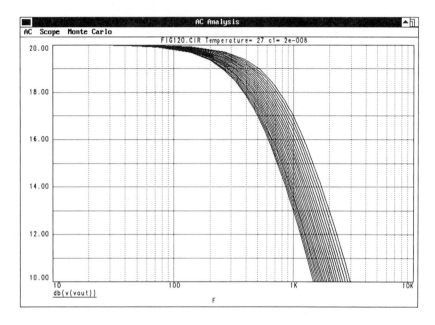

Figure 121

5. What is the dc gain and the corner frequency of the circuit shown in Figure 122?

   **Solution**: Input the circuit as shown. The result of the ac analysis is shown in Figure 123. The dc gain is 20.827 dB, and the corner frequency is at 2.8 kHz.

Figure 122

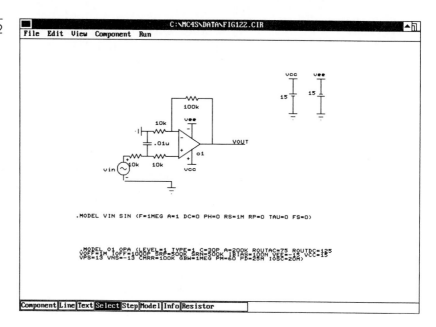

Figure 123

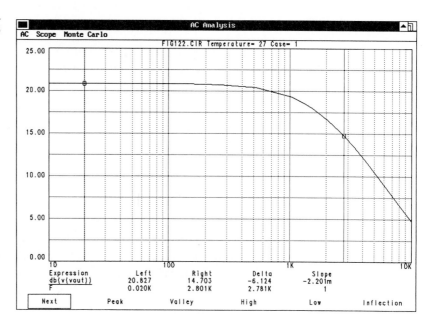

# Problems

1. Simulate a third-order Butterworth bandpass filter with

$$H(s) = \frac{s^3}{s^6 + 2s^5 + 5s^4 + 5s^3 + 5s^2 + 2s + 1}$$

   Plot the amplitude characteristic of this filter. What is the center frequency? Does this agree with the theory?

2. Plot the Nyquist diagram for the feedback system shown in Figure 53 (see Tutorial #1). The gain function of the amplifier is given by

$$A_d(s) = (19.2 \times 10^3) \left( \frac{S/0.1}{1 + S/0.1} \right) \left( \frac{S/0.5}{1 + S/0.5} \right) \left( \frac{S/5000}{1 + S/5000} \right)$$

3. An amplifier is shown in Figure 54 (see Tutorial #1). Determine the size of the two capacitors, C1 and C2, which will yield a low-frequency cutoff of 20 Hz.

4. Find the high-frequency cutoff for the 2N3903 transistor. Assume that the CE amplifier of Figure 55 (see Tutorial #1) is used with the emitter resistor bypassed.

5. A JFET amplifier is designed for a voltage gain of –10 and an input resistance of 50 k$\Omega$. The circuit is shown in Figure 56 (see Tutorial #1). Select the capacitor values for a lower-frequency cutoff of 20 Hz.

6. Examine the stability of a system with the following open loop transfer function:

$$G(s)\, H(s) = \frac{A}{s(s+1)\,(0.5s+1)}$$

   Do this by plotting the amplitude and phase, and finding the value of A that causes the gain to reach unity when the phase is –180°.

7. An RC highpass filter is shown in Figure 57 (see Tutorial #1). Design this filter for a high-frequency gain of 10 and a corner frequency of 1 kHz.

8. An active filter has a transfer function given by

$$H(s) = \frac{3s-10}{s+100}$$

What kind of filter is this?

9. Plot a Nyquist diagram for the circuit of Figure 58 (see Tutorial #1). To view the critical parts of the diagram, set the ranges of the real and imaginary parts to several microvolts.

10. Experiment with the following circuits, which are stored on your disk. When you execute the ac analysis using the stored limits, you will experience many of the functions available for MICRO-CAP IV.

**BPFILT.CIR**  A 3 op-amp bandpass filter with two offset stages. When you run this you will see what appear to be thick plot lines. This occurs since **Data points** was selected from the **Options** menu, so instead of just plotting the curve, the program draws dots.

**BUTTERN.CIR**  Shows a simple Butterworth lowpass filter simulated with a Laplace source.

**CROSSOVR.CIR**  A 1 kHz crossover network. The program will run multiple times for Monte Carlo analysis.

**L3.CIR**  A 20-pole Butterworth lowpass filter. It is simulated using a Laplace source. Note that we plot the dB gain, the phase, and the group delay.

**NOISEBJT.CIR**  Shows a plot of noise in a BJT.

**NYQUIST.CIR**  A demonstration of a simple Nyquist plot.

**P1.CIR**  Shows the use of a linear table source as an equivalent to a simple RC network. You can observe that the outputs are the same whether you use the circuit or the table source.

**TL2.CIR**  A transmission line circuit. This shows how to find frequency response of the circuit.

# 4

# DC Analysis

## Introduction

DC analysis evaluates input/output characteristics in the dc condition. The input can be a voltage appearing on a user-specified node (relative to ground) or a differential voltage between two nodes. Alternatively, the input can be a current source. The program evaluates the dc output, which can be either a voltage (for a node relative to ground or differential between two nodes) or a current flowing through a resistor specified by the two resistor nodes. The system replaces all inductors with short circuits and all capacitors with open circuits. It then applies a stepped dc source to the input and calculates the resulting dc output.

Begin by drawing a circuit on the screen, either by entering each component, as described in Tutorial #1 or by retrieving a network from the data file. Although you may use any circuit you have created, we illustrate dc analysis for the differential amplifier circuit. If you already have a circuit in the **Schematic Editor** window, begin by unloading this circuit using the **File** menu. Retrieve the differential amplifier circuit by pulling down the **File** menu, selecting *3:Load Schematic*, and then scrolling to DIFFAMP.CIR (recall that you can skip to the first "D" entry by typing **D**). Your screen should look like Figure 124.

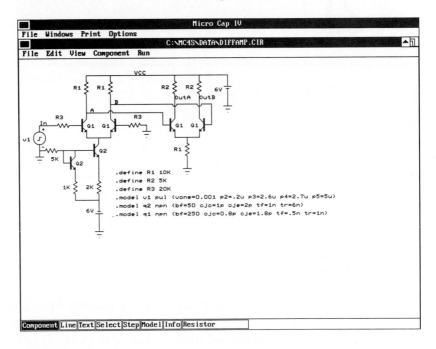

Figure 124

Once the network is on the screen, you initiate the analysis by pulling down the **Run** menu and selecting *3:DC analysis*. Alternatively, you can use the keyboard in one of two ways: Either type the menu identifier followed by the entry

**R; 3**

or use the hotkey (identified on the pull-down menu) by simply pressing Alt+**3**.

After you initiate the dc analysis, you are presented with the **DC Analysis Limits** window. We begin this tutorial with a discussion of this window. We then discuss each of the menu selections in the DC analysis.

# DC Analysis Limits

After activating the dc analysis, you are presented with a window showing 17 limits used in the analysis. When you store a circuit, the limits are stored with it. If you create a new circuit, default limits are used. The limits stored in the DIFFAMP circuit are shown in Figure 125.

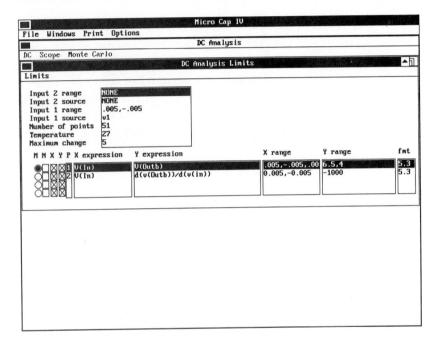

Figure 125

We now describe each of these analysis limits. However, if you are impatient to see an analysis run, you can simply pull down the **DC** menu (press Alt+**D**) and select *Run* (or press the F2 function key).

## Numeric Limits Fields

The upper portion of the window contains a field with seven entries.

### Input 2 range

The program has the capability of stepping two independent inputs. Input 2 is the secondary independent voltage/current sweep. The format is

**Final[,Initial[,Step]]**

The analysis starts at Initial and ends at Final. The system calculates solutions spaced equally over the range Final-Initial with spacing of Step. If you omit Step, this parameter defaults to Final-Initial. Therefore, the simulation runs twice, once at the initial value and once at the final value. If you omit Initial, this parameter defaults to zero.

If the secondary independent source is not used, enter **NONE**, as we have done in this example.

### Input 2 source

This determines where this input will be placed. The format is

**Plus[,Minus][,I or V]**

Plus is the node name or number of the node where the positive lead of the input source is to be connected. For current sources it can be thought of as the node toward which the directional arrow is pointing. Minus is the node name or number of the node where the negative lead of the input source is to be connected. The third field designates whether the input is a current source or a voltage source. The default for the third field is V (voltage source), and the default for Minus is ground.

Instead of specifying nodes, you could give the label of the source. For example, you might have a voltage source labeled "vin," in which case you simply enter that name.

### Input 1 range

This is the main input source. The format is the same as that for Input 2 range, except that the specified step size is the maximum step size. Thus the format is

**Final[,Initial[,MaxStep]]**

MaxStep is the maximum step possible during a sweep. The actual step size might be smaller since it is a function of the maximum change (the last entry in this field). The default value of Initial is zero. If you omit MaxStep, the program sets step values based on the maximum change. Note that Input 1 uses a variable step size while Input 2 uses a fixed step size.

### Input 1 source

This determines where the main input will be placed. The format is the same as that for Input 2.

### Number of points

This entry specifies the number of points calculated for numeric output. The default is 51, and the minimum is 5. Numeric output is calculated using linear interpolation of the simulated results. Hence the number of points requested for numeric output need not match the number of data points.

### Temperature

One or more temperature values can be specified for the analysis. The format is

**High[,Low[,Step]]**

The simulation is performed at temperatures between the Low and High, spaced by Step. Thus, for example, an input of **35,20,5** would produce separate runs at 20, 25, 30, and 35 degrees Celsius. If Step is omitted, two runs are performed, one at the Low and one at the High temperature. Thus the default value of Step is High–Low. If both the Step and Low are omitted, one run is performed at the High temperature. Thus the default value of Low is High.

### Maximum change

This field affects the size of the step taken by Input 1 during the simulation. A setting of 5% usually gives acceptable results. You might need a smaller step if device transitions (discontinuities in the input/output relationship) are involved. Of course, a smaller specification forces the simulator to take smaller steps and increases the time required for the simulation.

You can see from Figure 125 that the selected limits for this example are as follows:

- There is no secondary input.
- The main input is the voltage source, V1.
- The voltage source, V1, is stepped from $-0.005$ to $+0.005$ volts. Since no MaxStep is specified, the step size is set so that the maximum change is 5%.
- The simulation runs at one temperature, 27 degrees.

To change any of the analysis limits, click the mouse on that limit and then type in the new limit.

## Waveform Options Fields

We now turn our attention to the wide table occupying the lower half of the **DC Analysis Limits** window of Figure 125. The table contains ten columns. The first five of these are described below, and the remaining five are described in the next section.

### M

Enable the M (Monte Carlo) radio button if you want to perform a Monte Carlo analysis. Only one waveform can be selected for Monte Carlo analysis (that is, there can be only one dark button in the entire **M** column).

### N

The N (Numeric) column is in the form of a toggle box. It is used to select waveforms for numeric output. Numeric output is directed to a parallel or serial port, the screen, or to a file, depending on the selection made in the **Printer setup for text** window.

## X

This toggle box determines whether the X variable is linear or logarithmic. An X in the box indicates linear, while the absence of an X indicates the scale is a log scale.

## Y

This toggle box is the same as **X,** except it is for the Y variable.

## P

When several variables are plotted, you have a choice of superimposing them on the same set of axes or having them appear on separate nonoverlapping graphs. The numeric entry in the P column is a number from 1 to 9. This indicates to which group the particular waveform is assigned. If you use the same number for several rows, these waveforms are plotted on the same set of axes. If the ranges are not the same, the plot uses the union of the individual ranges.

The example of Figure 125 shows two curves plotted on two different sets of axes.

**Expression Fields**

The remaining five columns relate to the expressions to be plotted.

### X expression

This field specifies the expressions for the X-axis variable. Typical expressions are a voltage, say V(V1), or a current, I(V1), where V1 is the specified Input 1 source.

### Y expression

This field specifies the expressions for the Y-axis variable. This is typically a voltage or a current. Note that for the second curve, we specify a Y expression as a derivative, showing the rate of change of the voltage at Outb with respect to the voltage at in. This derivative is the slope of the first curve and represents the gain of the circuit.

### X range

This sets the scale ranges for the X waveforms. The format is

**High[,Low]**

In our example we run the simulation from −0.005 to +0.005 volts for input V(In), so our entry was **0.005, −0.005** for the X range. The default for Low is zero. You can type **auto** for this field, and MICRO-CAP IV automatically sets the range. In such cases MICRO-CAP IV must run a complete simulation before it can determine a suitable scale range. You can enter **auto** by placing the cursor on the appropriate field and typing **auto**. A faster way is to use the **Limits** menu, as discussed in the next section.

### Y range

This is the same as X range, except it is for the Y variable. You can enter **auto** for this field, and MICRO-CAP IV adjusts the range to fill the screen after running the simulation.

### fmt

This field controls the format of printed numbers used in the tabular printout or the cursor mode. The number to the left of the decimal point sets the space for digits to the left of the decimal point in the printed numbers. Similarly, the number to the right of the decimal point sets the number of digits to the right of the decimal point. The example shows 5.3, which means printouts will contain up to five digits to the left of the decimal point and three to the right (that is, thousandths).

**Limits Pull-Down Menu**

In the upper-left-hand corner of the **DC Analysis Limits** window is the **Limits** pull-down menu. The **Limits** menu contains two entries: *Default all* and *Default blank*. If you select *Default all*, the program inserts "auto" into all range fields with valid plot numbers. If you select *Default blank*, the program inserts "auto" into all blank range fields with valid plot numbers.

## Running the Analysis

Once you are satisfied with the analysis limits, you are ready to run the analysis. Run the analysis by pulling down the **DC** menu (using the mouse or by pressing Alt+**D**) and clicking on ***Run***. You can save all of this work by pressing the F2 function key. The dc analysis is produced, as shown in Figure 126. Note that seven separate simulations are performed. By now you should recognize this as a case of stepping. We examine stepping in the next section as part of the discussion of the **DC** menu.

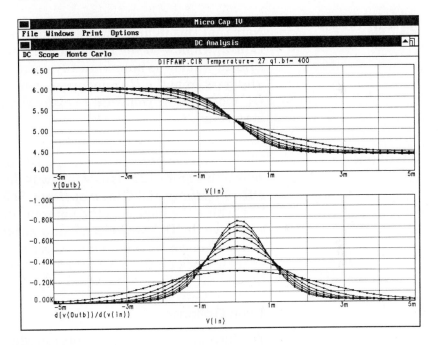

Figure 126

# DC Menu

Once you select **DC analysis** from the **Run** menu, you can pull down the **DC** menu either with the mouse, or if you are in a mode where this choice is not highlighted, you can always press Alt+**D**. The menu contains five selections.

> 1:Run
> 2:Limits
> 3:Options
> 4:Stepping
> 5:Numeric output

## 1:Run

You select this menu entry to run the simulation.

## 2:Limits

Note that this item is checked. It opens the **DC Analysis Limits** window so you can change limits. The **DC Analysis Limits** window is automatically opened when you select **DC analysis** from the **Run** menu, so you access **Limits** from the **DC** menu only if you want to make changes following a simulation run.

## 3:Options

Clicking on **Options** presents the **DC options** window, as shown in Figure 127. This window is divided into two areas: **1:Run options** and **Other options**. Selections may be made by clicking the mouse on the appropriate button or box. You can leave the **DC options** window either by initiating the run (pull down **DC** menu and select **Run**), by erasing the window (click on the box to the left of the title), or by pressing the Esc key.

### 1:Run Options

You have three choices: **Normal** produces a normal run. **Save** saves the entire simulation for later retrieval. **Retrieve** retrieves a saved simulation for review.

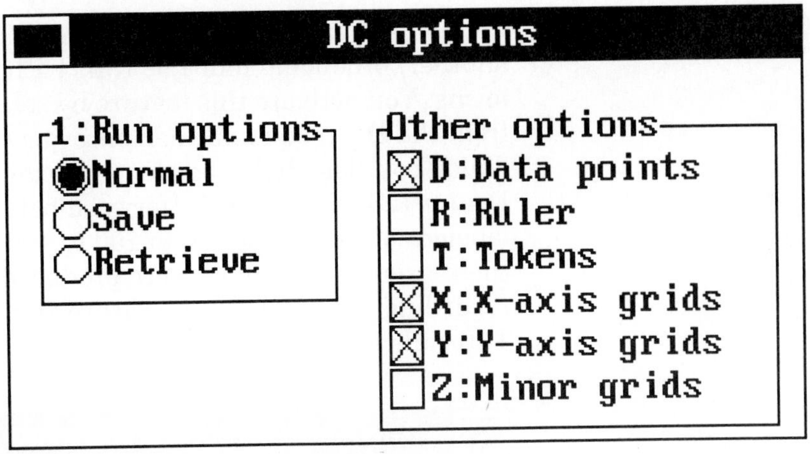

```
┌──────────────────────────────────────────────┐
│ ■        DC options                          │
├──────────────────────────────────────────────┤
│ ┌1:Run options┐   ┌Other options─────────┐  │
│ ●Normal          ⊠D:Data points          │  │
│ ○Save            □R:Ruler                 │  │
│ ○Retrieve        □T:Tokens                │  │
│                  ⊠X:X-axis grids          │  │
│                  ⊠Y:Y-axis grids          │  │
│                  □Z:Minor grids           │  │
└──────────────────────────────────────────────┘
```

Figure 127

## Other Options

This portion of the **DC options** menu contains six entries. These are the same as those in the **Transient options** and **AC options** menus.

*Data points*  Causes the actual data points of the simulation to be marked on the plot.

*Ruler*  Selects ruler marks in lieu of full-screen graph divider lines.

*Tokens*  Adds a token to all but the first waveform of each group. A corresponding token also appears on the axis scale to help in the identification process.

*X-axis grids*  Draws vertical grids or rule marks.

*Y-axis grids*  Draws horizontal grids or rule marks.

*Minor grids*  Used to switch the minor log grids (between powers of 10) on and off. It applies only to logarithmic scales.

**4:Stepping**

Component parameters may be stepped from one value to another, producing multiple runs with multiple output waveforms. You activate this feature by selecting *4:Stepping* from the **DC** menu and then entering instructions in the dialog box. The dialog box for this example is shown in Figure 128. Note that the forward beta of the transistors labeled "q1" is stepped from 100 to 400 in steps of 50. That is the reason seven curves were produced. If you need details regarding the entries in the **Stepping** window, refer to Tutorials #2 and #3.

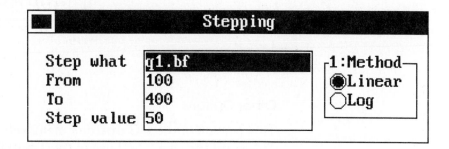

Figure 128

**5:Numeric Output**

If you have placed an X in the **N** column of the **DC Analysis Limits** menu, the numeric output is displayed as soon as you run the simulation. The display is in a window in front of the graphical output plots. You can remove the numeric window by pressing the Esc key. Once the window is removed, you can again activate it by selecting *5:Numeric output* from the **DC** menu.

## Scope Menu

The **Scope** pull-down menu is used to select various scope commands. The menu provides you with 11 choices. The menu selections and operation are identical whether you are performing a transient, ac, or dc analysis. Therefore, we will not repeat the menu description and instead refer you to Tutorial #2.

Figure 129 shows the scope display for the DIFFAMP circuit, where we have used the scope to find the peak of the output derivative curve. We have placed both cursors at the peak of the last curve produced. To locate this peak, we selected *Low* from the selections at the bottom (note that the ordinate decreases as you move up), positioned the cursor using the appropriate mouse button, and then pressed the arrow keys to move the left cursor to the peak, and the Shift+arrow keys to move the right cursor. Note that the peak occurs at an input voltage of 0.058 mV, and the value of the derivative at this point is –765. Since we have performed stepping in this analysis, the simulation produced a family of output curves. You can move the cursor from curve to curve using the up and down arrow keys.

## Probe

The PROBE tool is similar to that used in transient or ac analysis. The major difference is a greatly simplified list of choices for the variables. As an example, we will show the use of the probe mode for the DIFFAMP.CIR example. If you don't already have that circuit loaded, do so at this time. Then pull down the **Run** menu and click *4:Probe mode* so that there is a check in front of this entry. Then select *3:DC analysis*. Your screen should look like Figure 130.

If you pull down the **Vertical** menu in the **DC Analysis** window, you will find only two choices, *Voltage* and *Current*. You can also choose whether you wish the plot to be linear or log. The same choices exist for the horizontal axis. If we select *Voltage* for both of these, we can plot the voltage at the selected

Figure 129

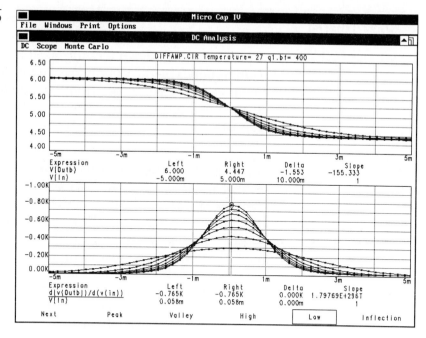

Figure 130

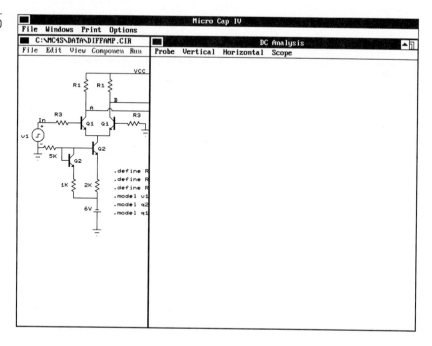

points as a function of the input voltage. If you have not already done so, remove the menu by pressing the Esc key. Then click the cursor on the point(s) you want to plot. As an example, we clicked on OutA and OutB to produce the curves of Figure 131. We also selected *Options* from the **Probe** pull-down menu, and then we selected *Tokens* so that the two curves can be distinguished from each other when a print copy is made (they are in different colors on the monitor).

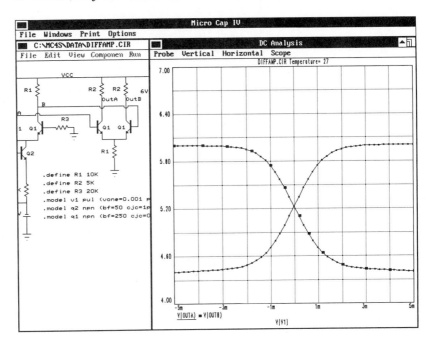

Figure 131

## Monte Carlo Analysis

The operation of Monte Carlo analysis is identical whether you are performing a transient, ac, or dc analysis. We therefore do not repeat the detailed discussion of Tutorial #2.

We shall perform one example to illustrate the process. Unload the DIFFAMP circuit and load the CARLO2 circuit. Your screen should look like Figure 132. This is an extremely

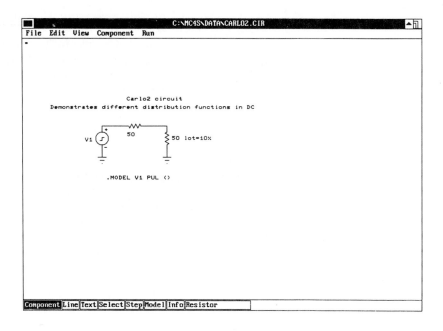

File   Edit   View   Component   Run

Carlo2 circuit
Demonstrates different distribution functions in DC

V1   50   50 lot=10%

.MODEL V1 PUL ()

Component Line Text Select Step Model Info Resistor

Figure 132

simple circuit. It is a voltage divider with a nominal divider
ratio of 1 to 2. The only nontrivial aspect of the circuit is that
the output resistor has a tolerance of 10% Now that the
circuit is loaded, select *3:DC analysis* from the **Run** menu,
and the **DC Analysis Limits** window is displayed. This is
shown in Figure 133.

Note that the M column has an **X** in it, so we are ready to
run a Monte Carlo analysis. The plot will show output voltage as a function of input voltage. The slope of the curve is
the divider ratio. We now need to pull down the **Monte
Carlo** menu to set the parameters. Do this either with the
mouse or by pressing Alt+**M**. Then select *1:Options* to display the **Monte Carlo options** window shown in Figure 134.

The numbers stored in the file produce a Monte Carlo analysis with 200 runs. The window is defined as running between
0 and 10 volts in both dimensions. This matches the ranges
in the **DC Analysis Limits** menu, so the window covers the

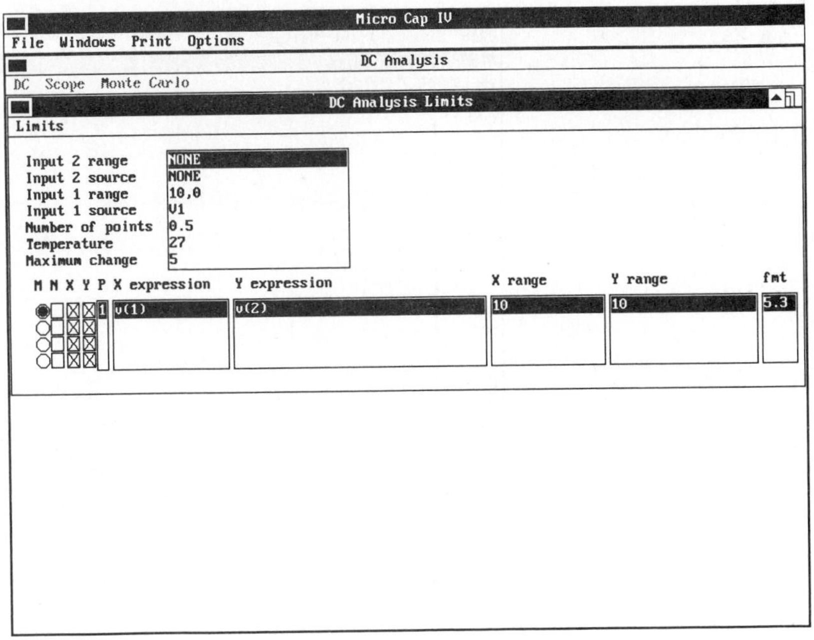

File  Windows  Print  Options

DC Analysis

DC  Scope  Monte Carlo

DC Analysis Limits

Limits

| Input 2 range | NONE |
| Input 2 source | NONE |
| Input 1 range | 10,0 |
| Input 1 source | V1 |
| Number of points | 0.5 |
| Temperature | 27 |
| Maximum change | 5 |

| M N X Y P X expression | Y expression | X range | Y range | fmt |
|---|---|---|---|---|
| 1 v(1) | v(2) | 10 | 10 | 5.3 |

Figure 133

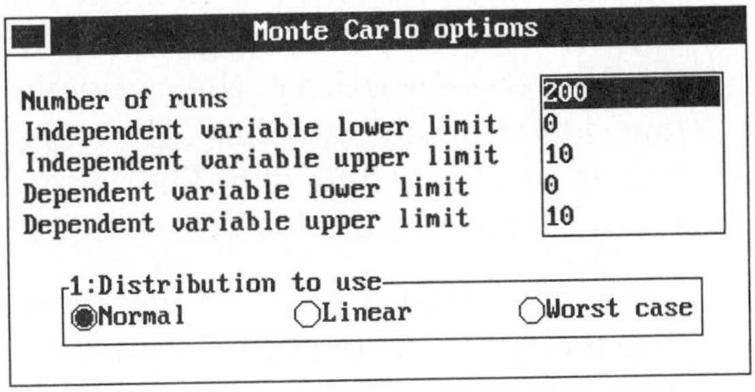

Monte Carlo options

| Number of runs | 200 |
| Independent variable lower limit | 0 |
| Independent variable upper limit | 10 |
| Dependent variable lower limit | 0 |
| Dependent variable upper limit | 10 |

1:Distribution to use
◉Normal      ○Linear          ○Worst case

Figure 134

entire screen. We have selected a normal (Gaussian) distribution for the resistor values.

When you run the simulation (press the F2 function key), the result is shown in Figure 135. The plot consists of 200 superimposed straight lines with varying slopes.

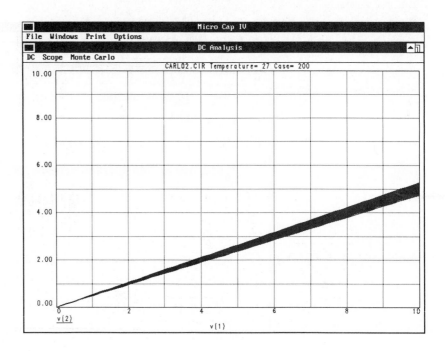

Figure 135

Pull down the **Monte Carlo** menu and select *2:Statistics*. If you select *Ymax* as the collating function, the histogram displays the statistics of the right end of each straight line (since the window matches the plotting range). This should have a nominal value of 5. The voltage divider ratio is one tenth of this parameter. The result is shown in Figure 136.

The mean value is 4.99 and the standard deviation is 0.098. The histogram is an approximation to a Gaussian density, which is expected since we specified a normal distribution in the **Monte Carlo options** window.

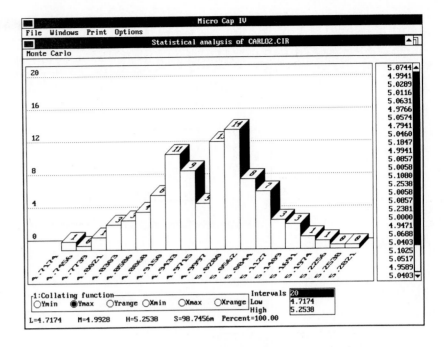

Figure 136

# Examples

1. You are given the nonlinear circuit shown in Figure 137. Find the input/output characteristic of this circuit.

   **Solution**: Run the dc simulation to plot the input/output relationship. After appropriate adjustment of the ranges of the variables, you obtain the graph of Figure 138. This shows that the circuit is a full-wave rectifier with a gain of approximately 1 for negative inputs and 3 for positive inputs.

2. Find the characteristics of the nonlinear circuit shown in Figure 139.

   **Solution**: Run the dc simulation to plot the input/output relationship. After appropriate adjustment of the ranges of the variables, you obtain the graph of Figure 140. This shows that the circuit is a half-wave rectifier with output of zero for positive inputs and -vin for negative inputs.

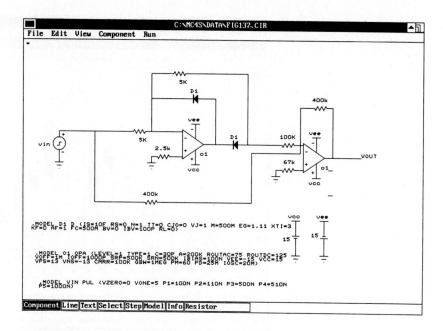

Figure 137

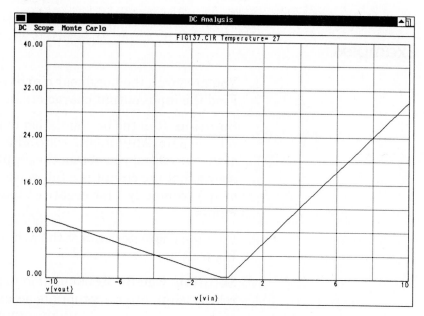

Figure 138

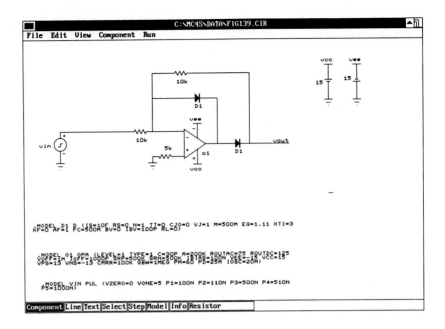

Figure 139

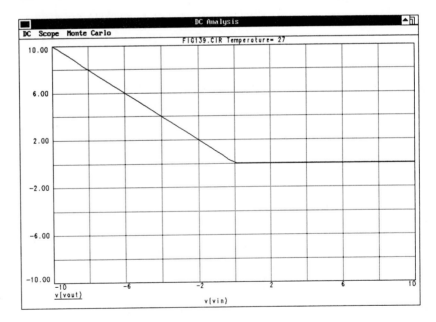

Figure 140

# Problems

1. What is the function of the circuit shown in Figure 59 (see Tutorial #1)?

2. What is the function of the circuit shown in Figure 60 (see Tutorial #1)?

3. Experiment with the following circuits, which are stored on your disk. When you execute the dc analysis using the stored limits, you will experience many of the functions available for MICRO-CAP IV.

   **IVBJT.CIR**  Illustrates BJT transistor collector current versus collector-to-emitter voltage with base current as a parameter.

   **IVMOS.CIR**  Illustrates operating curves for MOSFET transistors.

# III

## REFERENCE SECTION

# 1

# Error Messages

MICRO-CAP IV generates more than 150 error and warning messages. Below we list the most important of these in numerical order. We omit some categories where the error message is self-explanatory. The **bold** part is what appears on your screen. In these messages "text" means a specific identifier related to that operation. That is, the error statement will have the specific text within it instead of 'text' or 'text1' that we use in these definitions. The use of "i" and "j" means a specific number unique to that instruction or operation. In some cases an example is given, and such examples appear in [brackets].

**Error(1030.1)...in command line 'text'.**

Illegal or misspelled command-line option.

**Error(1040.3)...operand expected.**

This error is caused by a missing operand [2+].

**Error(1040.4)...in constant.**

An incomplete numeric value [1E-].

**Error(1040.7)...operator expected.**

A missing operator [sin()].

**Error(1040.18)...expression not allowed in function 'text'.**

Expression was found where a number was expected [V(2*3) instead of V(6)].

**Error(1081.2)...illegal use of 'text1' in 'text2'.**

In model statement when keyword LOT is placed before a model parameter rather than after it.

**Error(1081.6)...'text1' in 'text2'.**

In a .MODEL statement, model parameter numeric range check finds an illegal value
[.MODEL q1 npn(bf=−10)].

**Error(2025.1)...in parameter stepping instructions.**

Instructions in Stepping dialog box specify an unknown variable. Also occurs when **Log** option selected and Stepping dialog box specifies non-positive values.

**Error(2054.2)...internal time step too small in transient analysis.**

Program unable to converge at particular time point. If this happens, try the following changes in Global Preferences settings:
• Reduce the value of RELTOL.

• Increase the value of GMIN.

• Increase the value of ABSTOL.

• Increase the value of VNTOL.

• Change the model parameters for active devices.

**Error(2070.2)...waveforms in the same plot must have the same log/linear option.**

Two or more waveforms cannot appear on the same graph as some are linear and some are log.

**Error(2800.2)...insufficient memory.**

Usually occurs during analysis when the available memory is exhausted.

**Error(2800.5)...pivot too small.**

This error occurs when an abnormally small pivot value was encountered in the course of solving the equations. Enabling the *Pivot Solver* from the **Preferences** menu is sometimes helpful, but this error usually means that the circuit matrix is singular and cannot be solved.

**Error(2800.6)...failed to converge in specified number of iterations.**

Circuit operating point calculation did not converge to a stable solution. Try the following changes to the Global Preferences:

- Increase the value of ITL1.

- Reduce the value of RELTOL.

- Increase the value of GMIN.

- Change the model parameters for active devices.

# 2

# Keyboard Commands and Hotkeys

Although MICRO-CAP IV is a windows-type program that is most easily controlled using a mouse, the keyboard also can be used to run the various simulations. Even when using a mouse, you may find it convenient to use keyboard commands for some operations.

## Main Pull-Down Menus

When you first execute MICRO-CAP IV, you enter the Schematic Editor. Two sets of window pull-down menus are at the top of the screen. You can always pull down a menu by typing the first letter of the window name. Therefore, you type

**W** to pull down the main **Windows** menu

**P** to pull down the **Print** menu

**O** to pull down the **Options** menu

**F** to pull down the Schematic Editor **File** menu

**E** to pull down the Schematic Editor **Edit** menu

**V** to pull down the Schematic Editor **View** menu

**C** to pull down the Schematic Editor **Component** menu

**R** to pull down the Schematic Editor **Run** menu

Note that you cannot pull down the main window **File** menu until you close the current file by unloading the current schematic.

To pull down the window box (in the upper-left-hand corner of the window), press Alt+ the space bar.

Once you pull down a menu, you select the appropriate entry by typing the number or letter that begins that item in the menu. Some of the entries have hotkeys listed. The hotkeys are listed below:

| | |
|---|---|
| F1 | Help window |
| F3 | Quit MICRO-CAP IV |
| F4 | Cycle through open windows |
| F5 | Zoom active window |
| F8 | Find next |
| F9 | Toggle circuit scale |
| Ins | Add item |
| Del | Delete selected item |
| Home | Move circuit page left |
| End | Move circuit page right |
| Page up (PG UP) | Move circuit page up |
| Tab | Change to next item group |
| ↵ (Enter) | Add item/select submenu |
| Esc | Close window |
| Alt+F1 | Help for selected text line in SPICE editor |
| Alt+F2 | Print front window graphics |
| Alt+F3 | Print entire screen |
| Alt+F7 | Place active window in move mode |

| | |
|---|---|
| Alt+F8 | Place active window in resize mode |
| Shift+F4 | Cascade open windows |
| Shift+F5 | Tile active windows |
| Shift+Ins | Paste from clipboard to current cursor position |
| Shift+Del | Delete selected items and copy them to the clipboard (cut) |
| Shift+Tab | Change to previous item group |
| Shift+Backspace | Undo last command |
| Shift+Esc | Close window |
| Ctrl+Ins | Copy the selected items to the clipboard |
| Ctrl+Esc | Close window |

## Radio Buttons

Many of the windows in MICRO-CAP IV contain radio buttons. First you must select the group containing the radio button by pressing the Tab key to go forward through the list, or press Shift+Tab to go backward. If the item group has a character associated with it, you can type Alt+character to select the group. You then position the cursor under the desired radio button using the arrow keys. Finally, press the space bar to toggle the button.

## Toggle Boxes and Item Boxes

These are selected the same way as radio buttons, except that the arrow keys are not necessary because the box is the only item in the item group.

## Drawing Components

When you are in the Schematic Editor mode, you select components by pulling down the **Components** menu (type **C**) and then typing the number or letter next to the component you want to select. If the component contains a submenu (for example, *Active components*), you can scroll the submenu with the arrow keys. Once the item is highlighted, use the ↵ key to select it. After selecting the item, you can add it to the circuit at the cursor position by pressing Ins. The item is drawn on the screen, and you can move it using the arrow keys. You can reorient (rotate and flip) the component by pressing the space bar. Once you are satisfied with the location, press ↵. If the item requires a label, you then type that label followed by ↵. If a library exists for the selected component (for example, op-amps), you can select that library by using the Tab key to move to the + box, and then pressing space bar to activate the library.

## Analysis

Transient, ac, or dc analysis is activated from the **Run** pull-down menu. We have already described the method of pulling down menus and making selections. When the appropriate **Analysis Limits** window is activated, you need to scroll through this window and make changes to toggle boxes, radio buttons, and text items. Scrolling is done with the Tab and arrow keys, and entries are made using the space bar or, if text is required, by typing the entry. The run is executed by pressing F2. Close the window by pressing Esc, and exit the program by pressing F3.

# 3

# Conversion from MICRO-CAP III to MICRO-CAP IV

Your disk contains a program that converts circuit files and libraries from MICRO-CAP III to MICRO-CAP IV format. Additionally, it can convert SPICE text file device model libraries into MICRO-CAP IV binary format. To use the program that performs the conversion, you must not have deleted your old library files (LIBRARY.* or *.LBR MICRO-CAP III files).

The command-line syntax for running the conversion program is

**CONVERT[DRIVE:][PATH]NAME1**
**[DRIVE:][PATH]NAME2[.EXT]/MODE**

NAME1 is the name of the input file to be converted. You may prefix a drive and path, if desired. NAME2 is the name of the output file to be created. Both the name and the extension are optional. You may prefix a drive and path, if desired. If the name is omitted, the same name (NAME1) is used. MODE can be any one of the following:

**LIBRARY** Reads old model libraries and creates new MICRO-CAP IV libraries.

**CIRCUIT** Reads old MICRO-CAP III circuit files and creates new MICRO-CAP IV circuit files.

**SPICE** Reads a SPICE text device model file and creates a MICRO-CAP IV device model library file. The SPICE text file must contain a collection of one or more .MODEL statements.

**MERGE** Reads two MICRO-CAP IV model library files and merges them into a single file. This file is saved as NAME1.LBR.

As an example, suppose you want to convert all of your old MICRO-CAP III circuits into MICRO-CAP IV circuits. All of your old circuits are in a directory named MC3 and have an extension of .NET. You want to store the new files in the DATA subdirectory of the MC4S directory. You type

**CONVERT C:\MC3\*.NET C:\MC4S\DATA\ /CIRCUIT**

# Index

**Benjamin/Cummings License Agreement**

**READ THIS LICENSE AGREEMENT CAREFULLY *BEFORE* OPENING THE DISK POUCH. BY OPENING THE POUCH YOU ACCEPT THE TERMS OF THIS AGREEMENT.**

**IF YOU DO NOT ACCEPT OR AGREE TO THE TERMS OF THIS AGREEMENT, YOU MAY: (1) RETURN THIS UNOPENED PACKAGE WITHIN 10 DAYS WITH PROOF OF PAYMENT TO THE AUTHORIZED BOOKSTORE WHERE YOU TOOK DELIVERY; AND (2) GET A FULL REFUND OF THE LICENSE FEE.**

The Benjamin/Cummings Publishing Company ("Benjamin/Cummings") has authorized distribution of this copy of software to you pursuant to a license from Spectrum Software, Inc. ("Spectrum"), and retains the ownership of this copy of software. Spectrum retains the ownership of the software itself. This copy is *licensed* to you for use under the following conditions:

**Permitted Uses/*You MAY*:**

- Use this software only for educational purposes.

- Use the software on any compatible computer, provided the software is used on only one computer and by one user at a time.

- Use the software on a network, file server or virtual disk, provided that you have paid a license fee to use the software on each computer which executes the software's commands.

**Prohibited Uses/*You MAY NOT*:**

- Use this software for any purposes other than educational purposes.

- Make copies of the documentation or program disks, except as described in the documentation.

- Sell, distribute, rent, sub-license or lease the software or documentation.

- Alter, modify or adapt the software or documentation, including, but not limited to, translating, decompiling, disassembling, or creating derivative works.

This License and your right to use the software automatically terminate if you fail to comply with any provision of this License Agreement.

**General**

Benjamin/Cummings and Spectrum retain all rights not expressly granted. Nothing in this License Agreement constitutes a waiver of Benjamin/Cummings' or Spectrum's rights under the U.S. copyright laws or any other Federal or State law.

Should you have any questions concerning this Agreement, you may contact Benjamin/Cummings Publishing Company, Inc., by writing to: The Benjamin/Cummings Publishing Company, Inc., Electrical Engineering Editor, 390 Bridge Parkway, Redwood City, CA 94065.